Growing Up with
SCIENCE®

Third Edition

12

Railroad system–Seismology

Marshall Cavendish
Reference
New York

Marshall Cavendish
99 White Plains Road
Tarrytown, NY 10591

www.marshallcavendish.us

Library of Congress Cataloging-in-Publication Data

Growing up with science.— 3rd ed.
     p.   cm.
   Includes index.
   Contents: v. 1. Abrasive-Astronomy — v. 2. Atmosphere-Cable television —
v. 3. Cable travel-Cotton — v. 4. Crane-Electricity — v. 5 Electric motor-
Friction — v. 6. Fuel cell-Immune system — v. 7. Induction-Magnetism —
v. 8. Mapmaking-Mining and quarrying — v. 9. Missile and torpedo-Oil
exploration and refining — v. 10. Optics-Plant kingdom — v. 11. Plasma
physics-Radiotherapy — v. 12. Railroad system-Seismology — v. 13.
Semiconductor-Sports — v. 14. Spring-Thermography — v. 15. Thermometer-
Virus, biological — v. 16. Virus, computer-Zoology — v. 17. Index.
   ISBN 0-7614-7505-2 (set)
   ISBN 0-7614-7517-6 (vol. 12)
   1. Science—Encyclopedias.

Q121.G764 2006
503—dc22

                                                      2004049962
                                  09 08 07 06 05 6 5 4 3 2 1

Printed in China

CONSULTANT

Donald R. Franceschetti, Ph.D.
Dunavant Professor at the University of Memphis

Donald R. Franceschetti is a member of the American
Chemical Society, the American Physical Society, the
Cognitive Science Society, the History of Science Society,
and the Society for Neuroscience.

CONTRIBUTORS TO VOLUME 12

Chris Cooper   James Martin
Tom Jackson   Freddy Tipple

Marshall Cavendish

Editors: Peter Mavrikis and Susan Rescigno
Editorial Director: Paul Bernabeo
Production Manager: Alan Tsai

The Brown Reference Group

Editors: Leon Gray and Simon Hall
Designer: Sarah Williams
Picture Researcher: Helen Simm
Indexer: Kay Ollerenshaw
Illustrators: Darren Awuah and Mark Walker
Managing Editor: Bridget Giles
Art Director: Dave Goodman

CONTENTS

KEY TO COLOR CODING OF ARTICLES

 EARTH, SPACE, AND ENVIRONMENTAL SCIENCES

PHYSICS AND CHEMISTRY

LIFE SCIENCES AND MEDICINE

TECHNOLOGY

MATHEMATICS

PEOPLE

Railroad system

In the nineteenth century, railroads were the fastest way for people to travel long distances and for goods to be moved between places that were far apart. Now millions of people use railroad systems as the best way to commute to and from work in cities.

The first railroads were simple wooden tracks, and the first railroad cars were wagons pulled by people or horses. The wheels of the wagons had rims that kept them on the tracks and helped them roll along more easily. These early railroads were used mainly to haul coal out of mines.

Rails made of iron and engines powered by steam made it possible for railroads to carry enormous loads and many passengers at high speeds. The first railroads of this kind were developed in Britain in the early nineteenth century.

American railroad history

By the nineteenth century, there were a few horse-drawn railroads in the eastern United States. In 1815, New Jersey gave Colonel John Stevens (1749–1838) a contract to build a steam-powered railroad across the state. Stevens could not raise the money to do this, but he did build a small steam engine—the first in the United States. He made a successful test run in 1825, but it did not meet with acclaim.

Five years later, the Delaware and Hudson Canal Company of Pennsylvania built a railroad and imported a full-size locomotive from Britain—the first in North America. It ran on wooden tracks.

In 1830, a famous race took place between a horse and a locomotive called *Tom Thumb,* which was built by U.S. inventor, manufacturer, and philanthropist Peter Cooper (1791–1883). Cooper wanted to convince the management of the Baltimore and Ohio Railroad, which was being planned at the time, to use locomotives instead of horses. The horse won, even though the locomotive was much faster. *Tom Thumb* had been in the lead until the drive belt slipped and forced it to stop.

Nonetheless, the speed of the locomotive had been demonstrated. That same year, the South Carolina Canal and Railroad Company made the first trip with a steam-powered train. It traveled 6 miles (10 kilometers). In 1831, this railroad started the first regular U.S. passenger service between Charleston and Hamburg, South Carolina.

Growth and improvements

After 1830, railroads grew rapidly in the United States. By 1835, there were 1,000 miles (1,600 kilometers) of track. Although these railroads were owned privately, the federal government helped with their development. Congress felt that the railroads could help bring settlers to the parts of the country that needed them.

In 1850, the federal government gave grants of land to lay railroad tracks. The first track went from Chicago, Illinois, to Mobile, Alabama. It was

◀ *A freight train waits in sidings in Oregon. An extensive rail network links all the major cities in the United States, enabling the quick and efficient transportation of goods and people.*

◀ *During the American Civil War (1861–1865), railroads were valuable to both Confederate and Union forces. Each army could move a lot of troops and weapons by rail, and several battles were fought for control of the railroads.*

completed in 1856, and settlers poured into the region connected by the railroad. The success of the government-funded railroads brought more land grants. In return, the railroads had to promise to carry government property and troops at half fare and the national mail at four-fifths fare.

Trains had reached speeds of 50 to 60 miles (80 to 97 kilometers) per hour by the end of the nineteenth century. By this time, all tracks and rail cars were made of steel.

The first diesel-electric locomotive was put into service in 1925, but it was used only as a switch engine—one used to arrange railcars into trains. Diesel-electric trains were used for passenger services in 1934 and for freight trains in 1940.

Right across the whole land

The first railroad system to cross a continent was completed in 1869. It was made possible by the 1862 Pacific Railroad Act. This act gave two private companies huge tracts of land and millions of dollars to build the railroad. One of the two, the Central Pacific, started to build east from California, starting in 1863. The other, the Union Pacific, built west from Nebraska, starting in 1865. They met on May 10, 1869, at Promontory Point, Utah. A gold spike was driven to join the two lines, and great celebrations were held. By the end of the nineteenth century, four other transcontinental railroads had opened across the United States.

Around the world

Most of the world's major railroad lines had been built by 1870. The first was built in northern England in 1822. France started constructing one in 1827, and Germany followed in 1835. Canada's first railroad was built in 1836.

Russia completed the Trans-Siberian Railroad in 1916. This is still the longest single railroad line in the world, stretching 5,600 miles (9,010 kilometers) across Asia. The world's highest railroad crosses the Andes Mountains in South America. Building started in 1870, and it took many years to complete. The largest and busiest railroad networks in the world are in China and India.

Modern railroad systems

Modern-day travel by airplanes, long-distance trucks, buses, and automobiles has reduced the use of railroads, especially for long-distance passenger travel. However, trains are still an important means of transportation. Not only can trains travel very long distances, they can also carry thousands of tons of cargo. Trains that carry cargo are known as freight trains.

In addition, trains are vital to rapid transit systems, such as subway systems, in busy city centers. Commuter lines carry about 75 percent of all railroad users. It would take one thousand automobiles to transport the same number of people as one commuter train.

◀ *Railroad workers situated on and around two locomotives celebrate as two men shake hands to celebrate the joining of the Central Pacific and Union Pacific lines at Promontory, Utah, on May 10, 1869.*

These are short tracks branching off a main track, onto which a train moves to wait while another faster train passes. Trains need signals to tell them when it is safe to leave the siding. There are also junctions (points where two routes join), and traffic control must be used to keep trains from hitting each other at these junctions.

The following need to be taken into account to calculate the headway: the distance at which the driver can see the signal ahead, the length of the train, and the distance between one main signal and the one ahead.

Colored lights

Most signals for railroad traffic control are colored lights, similar to the signals on a street. These are attached to poles alongside or over the track so that they can be seen clearly from a distance. The bulbs used for these signals must be reliable. They contain a main filament (glowing wire) and an auxiliary filament. If the main filament burns out, the auxiliary takes over until the bulb can be replaced. If the auxiliary fails before a replacement can be made, an automatic relay device is released. This turns to red the signal in front of the one that has failed, stopping any oncoming train.

If train drivers were not given advance warning to stop, they would have to drive the trains at an extremely slow speed to avoid overshooting a red light. This advance warning, which is usually a yellow light, is given on a signal some distance before the main signal. The distance between signals is the length needed to stop the train (the braking distance). When a driver sees the caution light on the advance signal, he or she knows that the signal ahead is red and begins to brake.

Sometimes the signal consists of a semaphore instead of a light. This semaphore is rarely of the flag type. It is usually a movable arm on top of a pole. Each position of the arm has a meaning, as do each of the colored lights.

Intercity railroads make longer runs between cities and towns. These trains offer many comforts and services that subways and commuter trains do not. For example, they serve food and drinks, and some have sleeper carriages fitted with beds for overnight travel.

SAFETY FIRST

Most people are familiar with the system of traffic lights on the street, with red for stop and green for go. This system is meant to control traffic. Railroads also use lights and other signals to keep trains from running into each other.

All railroad traffic-control systems are designed to ensure that trains have enough headway, which means enough time and distance between two trains using the same track. On some busy commuter lines, the headway may be less than a minute. Even on intercity lines traveling longer distances, the headway during busy times can be just minutes. It is easy to see how trains could run into each other if the one behind fails to stop in time. Railroad signaling systems tell the trains when it is safe to travel at high speed.

Other hazards on a railroad include tunnels, steep hills, bridges, large bends, and roads that cross the track. Signals let drivers know when to slow down for these hazards. Railroads also have sidings.

Block signals

Railroad lines are divided into sections called blocks to make traffic control easier. Each block is 1 to 2 miles (1.6 to 3.2 kilometers) long. Only one train is allowed in one block at a time, and entry to the block is controlled by signals. A train can enter only when the all-clear signal is given. The block system can be operated manually or automatically.

Manual block signaling

Manual block signals are used only on old railroads that have not been updated for many years. An operator is stationed at various points along the line. Each signal controller takes care of one or two blocks and tells the other controllers by telephone when a block is clear.

People can make mistakes, however, so interlocking controls are used to prevent an accident in case of human error. Interlocking controls electrically connect a set of signals at the beginning of each block with the signals of the block ahead, as well as with all the other signals along the line.

When a warning signal shows that there is a train in the block ahead, all the signals in the block behind are automatically locked on red.

Automatic block signaling

Automatic block signaling works on the track circuit, which came into regular service in 1870. The track circuit is an electrical current flowing through the rails. When a train enters a block, it causes the track circuit to disconnect, and the signal automatically turns red to stop another train from entering the same block. As soon as the train leaves that block, the signals automatically turn to all-clear. Most of the automatic signals also have interlocking controls.

Centralized traffic control

So far, the traffic-control systems described have been for trains following each other on the same track. However, there are many other trains running on a rail network, and some overall traffic control is needed. Centralized Traffic Control (CTC) is the way in which railroad operators decide how to route the trains to various places so that they can travel at the greatest possible speed and with the greatest possible safety.

CTC operations take place at a central control center. Each center has a visual display showing the location of every train. The CTC operators study

◄ *Railroad tracks are connected by movable, curved rails, called switches, which direct trains from one track to another. Signaling systems are linked to the switches to prevent accidents from occurring.*

must turn off to confirm that he or she has seen the signal. Some trains are fitted with additional safety systems that apply the brakes automatically if the train passes a stop signal.

Generally, trains are equipped with two-way radios or telephones. Train crews use them to talk to each other, to get information from the stations ahead, or to talk to controllers.

MARSHALING YARDS

It takes careful planning and special equipment to ensure that railroad freight cars go to the right place to deliver the goods they carry. They are sorted out and made up into trains in an area called a marshaling, or classification, yard.

The marshaling yard is one of the busiest and largest parts of a railroad system. This is where freight trains are made up by arranging single freight cars according to their destination. It is also where cars that need repairs can be taken off the tracks and fixed.

A marshaling yard consists of many tracks, called sidings, that branch off from the main track coming into the yard. These tracks are parallel and set close together. The yard may be very large—some can hold as many as forty freight trains.

Each siding is used only for the cars that are going to the same area. After a complete freight train is made up on one of the sidings, it leaves along a main track at the other end of the yard.

▲ *The traffic on modern railroads is controlled using a system of red, yellow, and green signals. These tell train drivers if it is safe to continue (green), prepare to stop (yellow), or to stop completely (red).*

the display to decide which way each train should proceed toward its final destination and then set the necessary signals. About 20 percent of U.S. railroads use the CTC system.

The Location, Identification and Control (LIC) system of traffic control in Canada is similar to the CTC system in the United States. However, the LIC is based on radio links.

On-train signals

To help the train driver see the signals better, some trains can detect the signals they approach. Each signal sets off an alarm in the cab, which the driver

▶ *A railroad control room shows all the trains on a rail network. Controllers direct trains onto the correct track so they arrive at stations on time.*

▶ *Freight cars wait in a marshaling yard until they are ready to travel on the rail network.*

Making up the trains

Marshaling yards are usually operated by automatic machinery, which makes processing freight cars very efficient. Operators work in a control room that is similar to a control tower at an airport.

As a train arrives on the track leading into the marshaling yard, it is moved to the top of the hump, which is a specially built low hill or mound. As the cars move over the top of the hump, they are uncoupled (unlinked) so that they can roll down the other side of the hump. At this point, the computers switch them to the right track and also apply the retarders. Retarders are clamps that grip the wheels of the cars to slow them down. This controls their speed so that each car meets the one in front of it on the track with just the right amount of force to couple them.

The older type of marshaling yard was flat and had almost no automatic machinery. Switch engines hauled the cars from incoming trains onto the proper tracks and had to make many runs back and forth to break up and rearrange them. All the switches and railcar brakes were operated manually.

Recent methods

In the United States, it is now possible to make up freight trains with preblock cars. This means that from the very beginning, all the cars meant for the same terminal are arranged in groups, called blocks. They do not have to be repositioned again for the rest of their run.

Unit trains also do away with the need for large marshaling yards. These freight trains consist of the same type of freight car, carrying only one kind of goods. For example, they might all be open cars for coal, refrigerated cars for frozen food, or tank cars for oil. They might also make only regular nonstop trips between two particular points, such as from a coal mine to an electric power plant. The only change that might be necessary on unit trains is if locomotives and cabooses (brake cars) have to be switched for different lines.

TRAIN and ACI

Railroad companies keep track of their freight cars through a system called TeleRail Automated Information Network (TRAIN), which has its national center in Washington, D.C.

Cars also have automatic car identification (ACI) codes on their sides, which list type, owner, and number. Scanners along the tracks read the codes of the cars as they pass. This information is sent to the yard toward which the train is traveling.

See also: COG RAILROAD • LOCOMOTIVE • MONORAIL • RAPID TRANSIT SYSTEM • STEAM ENGINE

Rain and rainfall

The rain that falls from clouds provides the land with a supply of freshwater. Without this water, nearly all living things on land would not exist. In places with heavy rainfall, life-forms are very much in evidence. Where there is very little rain, the land is a dry, treeless desert.

Rain is a form of precipitation, which also includes dew, frost, hail, mist, sleet, and snow. All of these are formed from moisture in the air.

The Sun's heat evaporates moisture from the surface of the oceans. This moisture is turned into water vapor, which is carried upward by rising currents of warm air, where it gradually cools. Cold air cannot hold as much water vapor as warm air and, eventually, cooling air reaches the dew point, meaning that the air is saturated—that is, it contains all the water vapor it can at that temperature. Further cooling makes the air lose some of its vapor, which condenses (turns back into a liquid) to form tiny but visible droplets of water, or sometimes ice crystals.

Large numbers of water droplets or ice crystals form clouds. The clouds are blown over the land, where much of the moisture falls as rain or snow. Much of this water eventually returns to the sea through rivers or by seeping through rocks. This continuous process is called the water cycle.

How raindrops form

Raindrops can form in two ways. In warm regions, clouds are formed mainly of water droplets rather than ice crystals. These droplets are so tiny that they are suspended in the air. Upward air currents keep them from falling and, if they do fall, they soon evaporate in the warmer air below the clouds. However, in many clouds, the air is moving rapidly. The turbulent movements make droplets collide

▲ Rain is a common feature of the weather in much of the world. Rainwater is essential for most plants and animals. It waters the land and refills rivers and lakes.

and fuse together. Gradually, the droplets grow in size until they become raindrops. (One raindrop may contain up to one million water droplets.) When the raindrops are large enough, they fall to the ground, despite strong upward air currents.

In temperate areas, the clouds often contain many tiny ice crystals, together with water droplets that have been supercooled. During supercooling, the temperature of the droplets falls below the freezing point, but the droplets remain liquid and do not freeze into ice. However, when supercooled droplets come into contact with ice crystals, they immediately freeze onto the crystals.

The ice crystals thus grow in size, until they become heavy enough to fall. Near the ground, where the air is warmer, the crystals usually melt to become raindrops. If the air at ground level is cold enough, however, the crystals may not melt, and they will fall as snow, sleet, or hail.

Kinds of rainfall

For rain to form, moist air must rise and cool. In warm regions, the Sun heats the land in the morning. Evaporated moisture is swept upward by strong air currents, and dark cumulonimbus (storm) clouds develop in the afternoon, when thunderstorms may occur. This kind of rainfall is called convectional rain.

When moist winds from the sea reach land, they often have to rise over mountain ranges, which cools the air and causes clouds to form. Because of the high moisture content of the air, rain usually results. This rainfall is called orographic rain.

A third kind of rain, common in temperate regions, is called cyclonic rain. This rain forms in large air systems called cyclones or depressions. Depressions contain bodies of cold and warm air. The boundaries between them, called fronts, are

▲ *This huge rain forest in South America has formed largely because of the high levels of rainfall in the region. Rain forests sustain the greatest variety of life anywhere on the surface of Earth.*

places where the warm (light) air rises above the cold (heavy) air. Clouds then form, and rain falls from the clouds along the fronts.

Distribution of rainfall

Much of the rainfall in temperature regions is cyclonic, much of the rainfall in equatorial regions is convectional, and much of the rain in mountain regions is orographic. All occur because air is rising.

In some parts of the world, air tends to sink rather than rise. In tropical and subtropical areas, sinking air becomes warmer as it descends, so it can hold more and more water vapor. Such regions are deserts. Cold air also sinks downward near the poles, so these regions also have little precipitation. They are often called polar deserts.

See also: CLOUD • CYCLONE • SNOW AND FROST • THUNDERSTORM • WATER • WATER CYCLE • WEATHER SYSTEM • WIND

Rainbow

Rainbows are beautiful arcs of colors in the sky. They can be seen when the Sun shines on part of the sky where there are many drops of water, such as raindrops, or even on the spray given off by lawn sprinklers and waterfalls.

Rainbows occur when the Sun's rays are reflected (bounced back) and refracted (bent) by drops of water in the air. Sunlight is a combination of the colors of the spectrum—that is, it contains red, orange, yellow, green, blue, indigo, and violet. These are the colors that appear in a

▼ *This primary rainbow has appeared over a mountain range. The seven colors of the spectrum can be seen, from red on the outside, through orange, yellow, green, blue, and indigo to violet on the inside.*

rainbow, although they often overlap and blend into each other, so that only four or five of the seven colors are actually visible.

How rainbows form

Rainbows are seen when looking away from the Sun as it shines on a part of the sky filled with raindrops. Each raindrop acts like a prism—a piece of glass or other transparent material cut with precise angles and plane faces that can separate white light into its constituent colors. Rays of sunlight are refracted as they enter a raindrop and split into the colors of the spectrum. The far side of the raindrop reflects the rays. On leaving the raindrop, the light is further refracted. Rays entering near the center and the edges of the raindrop are refracted by nearly 180 degrees. Rays entering between the center and the edges are refracted through less of an angle. The angle is also different for each color.

▲ *The rainbow in this photograph is seen over a river gorge. The moisture in the air above the river provides the conditions for the rainbow to be observed.*

DID YOU KNOW?

The height of a rainbow above the horizon depends on the altitude of the Sun. When the Sun is low, a rainbow is high. When the Sun is high, a rainbow is low—perhaps even below the horizon. French mathematician René Descartes (1596–1650) calculated that rainbow arcs appear roughly 42 degrees above the antisolar point, which is the point on the ground that lies directly opposite the Sun from an observer. To find a rainbow, an observer should place her back to the Sun. The spot on the ground where the shadow of the observer's head is cast marks the antisolar point. To approximate 42 degrees above this point, the observer can stack four fists, held at arm's length, on top of the head shadow. Above the fourth fist will be where a rainbow may appear.

Complete rainbows contain two bands of color. The primary bow, the most distinct, displays red on the outside and violet on the inside of the arc. The outer, less distinct secondary bow has the colors in reverse order, with violet on the outside and red on the inside. Secondary rainbows have two refractions and two reflections inside the raindrops, which reverse the colors displayed.

The higher the Sun is in the sky, the lower the rainbow. If the Sun is higher than 42 degrees above the horizon, no rainbow will be seen. At sunset and sunrise, an observer in an airplane may see the complete semicircle of a rainbow. Moonlight may also cause rainbows. Such rainbows are faint, because moonlight is less intense than sunlight.

See also: LIGHT • RAIN AND RAINFALL

Rapid transit system

A rapid transit system is a transportation network that can move large numbers of people. Rapid transit systems are found in large cities and are designed to meet the needs of commuters—workers who travel to city centers in the morning and then return home in the evening.

Electric railroads are at the center of most rapid transit systems. Rapid transit lines may run underground (subway), above street level (elevated transit line), or at street level. The stations on a rapid transit system are much closer together than the stations of regular railroads, so passengers can get on and off the train near where they live or work. At busy times, trains arrive every few minutes to collect the many thousands of people who travel at the same time.

Unlike other forms of transportation, such as automobiles or buses, rapid transit vehicles travel along a route that is open only to them. No other vehicle or any pedestrians can access the route, and therefore the risk of delays is minimized.

Some cities have rapid transit systems that do not use trains. Instead they use streetcars (known as trams in Europe) and electric trolleybuses running along reserved lanes in the street.

Streetcars and trolleybuses

Streetcars run on tracks in the road. The first were built in the mid-nineteenth century and were pulled by horses. By the twentieth century, however, most were powered by electric motors that received electricity through overhead wires. A device called a trolley made contact with the wires, and streetcars also became known as trolleycars.

Trolleybuses do not run along tracks. Instead, they drive on tires similar to regular city buses, with the driver steering with a steering wheel. However, trolleybuses are powered by overhead wires. Sometimes, a few trolleybuses are connected together to make short trains.

Light railways

The main differences between light railways and regular railroads is that light railways run on a narrower gauge—the tracks are closer together—and the engines and cars are smaller and lighter. Light railroads are easier to lay through urban areas

◀ A train crosses La Salle Street in Chicago. Chicago has the largest elevated railroad in the world.

because bridges and elevated sections are cheaper to build. Some light railroad lines are monorail systems, in which the cars sit on a wide central rail. Many elevated railroads are monorails.

Subway systems

The largest rapid transit systems operate electric passenger trains. The tracks mostly run in underground tunnels, but they also carry trains over

▼ *This map shows a section of the MetroLink light railroad system, running from downtown East St. Louis, Illinois, through St. Louis, Missouri, to the Lambert-St. Louis municipal airport. The system opened in 1993 at a cost of $346 million.*

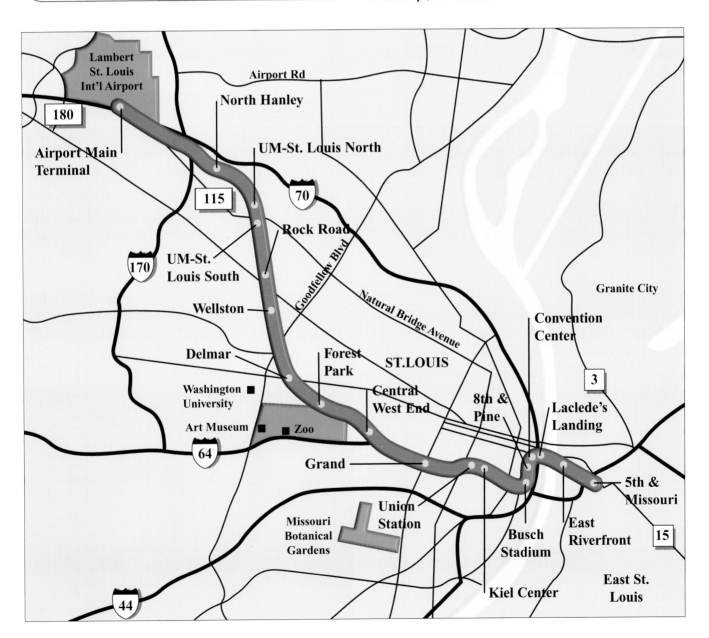

◀ The Chicago L (short for Chicago Elevated) is a rapid transit system serving Chicago and its suburbs. The oldest segments of the Chicago L date to 1892, while the most recent extension, the Orange Line to Midway Airport, opened in 1993.

elevated sections or at street level. Subway systems—also called tubes or metros—help people avoid the crowded streets of busy city centers, carrying hundreds of thousands of passengers every hour.

Tunnel under traffic

Underground railroads were first used in mine tunnels to carry workers and materials. The first to be built to transport passengers opened in London in 1863. At 3¾ miles (6 kilometers) long, this railroad was seen as an answer to the problem of congestion. Over the next century, subways were built under many of the world's large cities.

Most of the London Tube travels through deep tunnels. However, later subway systems, including the Paris Métro and the subway under New York City, travel through tunnels dug just beneath street level. These tunnels were dug using the cut-and-cover method, which is still used to construct many modern subway systems.

In this method, long, deep trenches are dug along main roads on the desired route. They are lined with brick or concrete and given a roof of strong steel girders on which a new road or building can be constructed. The cut-and-cover method is an inexpensive way of making tunnels. To avoid too much disruption to road traffic, trenches are dug and then covered in small sections.

▶ A train pulls into a station of the Washington, D.C. subway system. The first stretch of this subway opened in 1976. The final station was completed in 2001.

Boring tunnels

Deeper tunnels are much more complex and expensive to build. Boring through solid rock takes a long time, while tunnels often collapse when cutting through softer soil. In 1818, French-born British engineer Marc Isambard Brunel (1769–1849) developed a system for digging through soft earth using a tunneling shield. The shield was a moving framework that supported the soft tunnel while it was being dug—long enough for supports to be put in place. Brunel used his tunneling shield to drive a tunnel through the clay beneath the Thames River, London. This tunnel later became part of the London Tube network and is still in use.

Tunneling shields also were used to build London's underground railroads. The shields were large steel cylinders with sharp front edges. Powerful rams pushed the shield forward 18 inches (45 centimeters) at a time, while miners excavated soil from the center of the cylinder. Iron or concrete rings were used to line the tunnel; the rams pushed against the rings to nudge the shield forward.

This tunneling technique was used until the 1950s, when boring machines replaced shields as the main way to dig deep tunnels. The boring machine works in a similar way to a giant drill, using a large spinning head to cut through soil.

Trains

Electric trains were first used in subways in 1890. The first trains were pulled by a single locomotive engine, but modern trains are multiple-unit electric trains. The electric motors are fixed into the floor units of each passenger car. In this way, the power is more evenly spread throughout the train, and the wheels are less likely to slip. The electricity is supplied to the train through overhead wires or a third rail. A flexible device, called a pantograph, connects each railcar to overhead wires. In the case of third rails, electricity flows into the motor through a contact, called a shoe.

Modern trains used in rapid transit systems are often very crowded. As a result, they must be able to pick up speed rapidly and brake fast without causing the passengers too much discomfort. Because the stops are frequent and the distances between them short, the trains rarely reach very high speeds—an overall speed of 20 miles (32 kilometers) per hour is usual in city centers. In the suburbs, where stations are farther apart, speeds are a little faster. As a result, the time it takes for a train to complete a journey mostly depends on how long the driver must wait in stations for passengers to get on and off the trains.

Lightweight trains use either rheostatic or regenerative braking to bring the speed down and then use mechanical brakes to stop. Rheostatic braking uses the electric motors as electricity generators to absorb the energy of the train's motion. The electrical power produced is removed as heat through resistances. Regenerative braking follows the same system but channels the power back into the rail network to run other trains farther up the line.

Subway safety

Safety is one of the most important features in running any rail system and is especially important in an underground service. The small space makes rescue work and repairs extremely difficult.

Train drivers follow signals in the form of colored lights. The signals change automatically as trains pass through "track circuits." A small

▲ Subway trains such as the Singapore Mass Rapid Transit (SMRT) train are designed to carry as many passengers as possible. Only a few seats are provided; other passengers have to stand for the journey.

electrical current in the rails is interrupted by a train passing over the section, or block, in the line. This triggers the light behind to show a stop signal. The lights only change once the train has passed through another block farther up the line.

An extra safeguard is provided by a "train stop" a short way past each signal. This is an arm that is raised or lowered by an electric motor or compressed air. When the signal is red (stop), the arm is raised; if the signal is green (safe to continue), the arm stays down. If a train passes a red signal, it catches the arm and triggers the brakes.

Automatic trains

A number of rapid transit systems operate automatic trains that do not need drivers. The train cannot see colored signals. Instead, coded impulses pass through the rails. The impulses are picked up by the train to ensure that the track ahead is clear. A computer uses the impulses to control the position and speed of all the trains on the network.

See also: MONORAIL • RAILROAD SYSTEM • STREETCAR AND BUS

Recycling

Many of the items that are thrown away every day can be recycled. Old newspapers, metal cans, glass jars, and bottles can be collected and broken up. By cleaning and processing them, these materials can be reused.

A serious problem in most towns and cities is what to do with the huge amounts of trash that result from humankind's modern, disposable lifestyle. Up until quite recently, burying, dumping in the sea, or burning were the main ways to dispose of trash. The problem with these solutions, however, is that they are not environmentally "friendly." The problem is made worse because of the increasing amounts of waste worldwide.

Paper, wood, cardboard, rags, and some other materials can be burned. They will also rot and can even be of some benefit to the soil. However, metals do not burn easily. They take a long time to rust away, and while disintegrating they are an eyesore.

Glass does not rot either, and although it does neither harm nor good to the soil or water, broken glass is always dangerous. Waste oils can be dangerous and can pollute the air, rivers, lakes, and soil. Plastics, which are being produced on an ever-increasing scale, present great problems when it comes to their disposal, because they are almost indestructible.

Recycling makes sense

Many of the world's metals are becoming scarce, and larger areas of forest are being cut down every year for timber. Recycling materials such as paper is therefore becoming more important. There is also the advantage of not having to turn raw materials into finished products. It takes 17 large trees, 275 pounds (124.5 kilograms) of sulfur, 350 pounds (158.5 kilograms) of limestone, 60,000 gallons (272,760 liters) of water, and 9,000 pounds (4,082 kilograms) of steam, plus a lot of electricity, to make just 1 ton (0.9 tonnes) of paper.

Paper

Most paper can be recycled, although some kinds can be more difficult to recycle than others. Waste-paper makes up the largest part of household trash. Large amounts of paper are also wasted by factories, stores, and offices. There are many kinds of papers that can be recycled. There are newspapers, magazines, paper bags, and wrapping paper, as well as all kinds of packaging cardboard and paper mixed with other materials. However, collecting, transporting, and sorting paper can

◄ *Cranes and mechanical claws at the Bridgeport RESCO power plant in Connecticut dry out vast piles of garbage. The waste is then fed into an incinerator to produce useful energy.*

be expensive. Therefore it is sometimes not worthwhile to collect paper unless it can be done on a very large scale, which keeps the final price of the recycled paper low.

New paper from old

After sorting, the used paper is converted into pulp, and chemicals are added to remove any unwanted material. Printing ink is removed by washing and bleaching, although up to one-quarter of the paper pulp can be lost in the process. Since the fibers of reprocessed paper are weaker than those of new wood pulp, recycled paper does not have as many uses as new paper. Often, new wood pulp is added to the reprocessed pulp to strengthen it. On the other hand, the paper may have been processed before, and second or third reprocessing will make its fibers even weaker. One of the defects of recycled paper is that it is less dense than new paper. It also soaks up moisture, which makes it ideal for use in the domestic tissue industry.

Metals

Metal recycling is a valuable industry. The high cost of extracting the raw materials from which iron, aluminum, tin, and other metals are produced means that costs can be cut if these metals can be reclaimed from scrap.

Large amounts of iron and steel are recycled. Apart from being used to make cast iron objects, iron is mainly used in steelmaking. Iron and steel scraps are sorted, graded, and treated for the removal of other metals and materials. There may be tin plating on steel food cans, for example, or aluminum and plastic trimming on automobiles. The scrap metal is then put into the furnace with iron ore and reprocessed into steel. The quality of the finished recycled steel is almost identical to that of steel made directly from raw materials.

Aluminum, particularly the aluminum in cans and foil, is another metal that represents a huge saving when recycled. Around 95 percent of the energy used to make aluminum from its ore (bauxite; Al_2O_3) is saved with the recycled metal.

▲ **To be recycled, different kinds of trash must be separated, which is difficult to do with bulk trash. For recycling to be most effective, people need to be encouraged to get involved in the process.**

Other metals that are recycled are lead, mercury, and copper, as well as precious metals, such as gold, platinum, and the large amounts of silver recovered from the photographic industry.

Glass

Glass is made from silica (sand; SiO_2), limestone ($CaCO_3$), and salt (NaCl). There are plenty of these raw materials in the world, so it is not because of scarcity that glass is recycled. By reusing glass, however, there are savings in energy and money. There are laws in a number of states in the United States, as well as in Canada and Australia, that encourage the return and reuse of bottles and cans. Large containers, sometimes called bottle banks, are placed in towns and cities where the public can put empty bottles ready for collection.

Reusing glass

Recycled glass is first separated according to color and quality so that it is the same as the new glass batch into which it will be mixed. It is then crushed into pieces called cullet. The cullet goes through several stages to remove metal, plastic, or any other trash. It is then added to the new molten glass. Other uses for the crushed glass are in road construction, in landfill on construction sites, or in the manufacture of abrasives.

Plastics

Unlike paper and cardboard, plastics will not decompose when thrown away, and some plastics are dangerous to burn because they produce poisonous fumes. Therefore, it makes sense to recycle as much of these materials as possible. Most of the plastics produced today are called thermoplastics, which soften when heated and harden when cooled. Unfortunately, there are many different kinds of thermoplastics, and they must be completely separated if high-quality recycled plastics are to be produced.

As yet, there is no way to recover mixed plastic packaging waste, nor can plastics be recovered on any scale from household trash. Where large amounts of plastics can be easily recovered, recycling is little more than melting and reusing. Some plastics, such as chlorinated polyethylene (CPE), are known to be able to help plastics of many kinds to mix together when melted.

Oil

Oil is one of Earth's most valuable natural resources. According to some estimates, oil will run out toward the end of the twenty-first century. However, much can be done to cut down the hundreds of millions of gallons of used oil that are disposed of in industrialized countries each year. By recycling oils, huge savings could be made over new oil, and there would not be as much pollution of land and water as a result of their disposal.

Recycled oil

The recycling of oil is still relatively small-scale, and experiments are being conducted to explore new methods of recycling oils. However, oil recycling has proved successful. Sometimes oil needs only cleaning for it to be reusable. If the oil has undergone chemical changes, then it will need reprocessing. In addition to being used for further lubrication, it can also be used to make other oil-based products, such as agricultural chemicals, detergents, antifreeze, dyes, and plastics.

Using recycled oil for heating

There is much interest in finding ways to use recycled lubricating oils in place of expensive heating oil. One way that has worked in high-temperature furnaces is to mix the lubricating oil with small amounts of fuel oil. On a smaller scale, new heaters have been developed for use in workplaces and large reception areas. These heaters are designed so that all the fuel is burned without smell or fumes. One of these heaters thins the oil

◄ *Glass bottles are easy to recycle, and the finished glass is almost as good as new. Many towns and cities have bottle banks where people can recycle glass.*

▶ *Workers sort through pieces of different colored glass at the Tönsmeier recycling plant in Porta Westfalica, Germany.*

and then breaks it up into tiny droplets using compressed air. The fine oil spray is burned, and it is difficult to tell the difference between the flame produced by unused fuel oil and the recycled lubricating oil.

Since lubricating oils may contain certain substances added to make them better at lubricating, they must be checked carefully. The oils also have to be filtered before they are fed to the burners. This process removes any specks of metal or other material that may have dropped into them from the machinery they were lubricating.

SEPARATION

In spite of efforts such as bottle banks and waste-paper collection, recycling relies on separating useful materials from bulk trash collection. Several types of machines are used for separating the different materials from the trash.

Separating by stages

In stage separation, all the trash is shredded and then dried. Next, the chemicals in the materials of the trash are broken down by heat in a process called pyrolysis. Food waste, plastics, paper, and all materials made from once-living matter are turned into charcoal. When cool, the trash is broken into smaller pieces, and powerful magnets remove all the iron-containing metals. The remaining materials are separated into large and small pieces, and all the charred pieces are removed by powerful jets of air. Glass, aluminum, and other metals are then removed. The mixed pieces of glass are further separated into colored and clear glass. Colored glass is then separated into different shades.

The rotor method

Other separators have different methods for sorting out the various materials. The ballistic separator is a chamber with a rotor—a section of the floor that spins around—in the center, on which trash is dumped. The rotor spins and throws the trash, which has been broken up into pieces roughly the same size, into the chamber. The heavy pieces, such as metal and glass, are flung further than the lighter materials such as paper, plastics, and wood, and thus they can be separated.

The conveyor-belt method

Among other separators is the inclined plate separator. In this machine, trash is scattered onto a conveyor belt traveling upward at an angle. Heavier materials roll down to the bottom of the conveyor, while lighter materials are carried to the top.

See also: ECOLOGY • GLASS • METAL • PAPER AND PAPERMAKING • PLASTIC

Reflection and refraction

A person sees an object when light bounces off the surface of the object and into the person's eyes. This process is called reflection. Whenever light passes between two different substances, such as air and water or air and glass, the light changes the direction in which it is moving. This process is called refraction. Reflection and refraction make it possible for people to see an object, and they affect how the object is perceived.

▲ *A technician inspects the aluminum coating of the Gemini North mirror at the Mauna Kea Observatory in Hawaii. Astronomical telescopes can show billions of stars and galaxies that the unaided eye cannot see.*

There are many different forms of wave motion. Ripples on a pond are waves in water. Sound is waves moving through air, water, or a solid. Light from the Sun also moves as waves. Light is a form of electromagnetic radiation, similar to gamma rays, microwaves, radio waves, and X-rays. Unlike sound or the wave motion in water, electromagnetic waves can move through empty space.

Waves change their direction of movement when they strike objects. Some of the waves bounce off of the object in a process called reflection. Sound waves are reflected from buildings and can be heard as echoes. Objects reflect light waves, too. When a person sees an object, he or she is really seeing the light waves reflected from that object.

What is reflection?

If a person shines a flashlight beam onto a piece of paper in a dark room, the reflected light travels in all directions from the paper. This sort of reflection is called diffuse reflection (the word *diffuse* means "spread out"). If instead a person shines the flashlight beam onto a mirror hanging on a wall, he or she will see the beam being reflected from the smooth metal surface at the back of the mirror. When the light rays spread out from the flashlight beam and strike the mirror, it seems as if they are coming from a second flashlight situated behind the mirror. The image on the mirror is in fact a reflection of the flashlight in front of the mirror.

Using mirrors

People use mirrors in countless ways. For example, mirrors in an automobile provide the driver with a view behind the vehicle without the driver having to turn his or her head. This type of mirror is convex, which means it is thicker in the center than at the edges. The convex mirrors of an automobile show the area behind the vehicle "squeezed" into a smaller angle of view.

A bathroom mirror is often concave, which means it is thinner in the center than at the edges. Concave mirrors provide a magnified image of the face of the person looking into the mirror, useful when shaving or applying makeup. The large mirrors in astronomical telescopes are also concave. They give magnified images of objects in space, such as galaxies, planets, and stars. Just as important, they gather large quantities of light, making faint objects seem brighter. The dishes of

▶ *A convex lens refracts parallel beams of different colored light into a single spot behind the lens.*

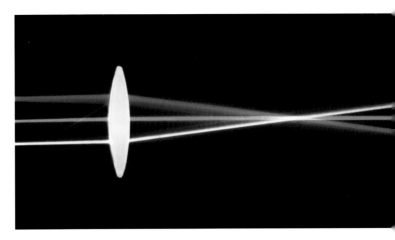

radio telescopes are concave mirrors. They are designed to gather radio waves from space. Radar dishes and satellite television dishes do the same job for radar and television waves.

Refraction

When light strikes a transparent (clear) material, such as glass or water, some of the light is reflected. However, some of the light also passes through the material and emerges from the other side. If the light travels through one clear material into another clear material of a different density, it will bend in a process called refraction. It is the change in the speed of the light passing from one material to another that changes the direction of motion. As the light waves travel from air into a denser material such as glass or water, the light waves slow down, and the beam bends into the material. As the light waves emerge from the glass or water into air, which is less dense, the light waves speed up and bend back in the opposite direction.

The effects of refraction are common in everyday life. For example, a straight straw in a glass of water appears to bend at the point at which it enters the water. Similarly, a swimming pool seems to be shallower than it really is, and the parts of the bodies of swimmers that are below the water seem much shorter than they actually are.

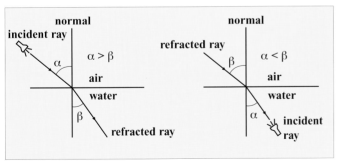

▲ *This diagram shows the principles of refraction. Light bends as it passes from one clear material into another clear material of different density. When light passes from air into water (left), the angle of incidence (α) is greater than the angle of refraction (β). When light passes from water into air (right), the angle of incidence (α) is less than the angle of refraction (β).*

> ### DID YOU KNOW?
>
> Mirages are caused by refraction. On a hot day, for example, there may be a layer of hot air just above the surface of a highway. Light travels slightly faster in hot air than it does in cold air, so sunlight entering the layer at a nearly horizontal angle can be bent upward toward someone observing from a distance. The person will see what looks like the reflection of the sky on the road—as if caused by a pool of water.

Using refraction

The lenses that are used in optical instruments such as cameras are designed to make use of refraction. Convex lenses are thicker in the middle than at the edges. When parallel rays of light pass through a convex lens, they converge or come together at a single spot behind the lens. Lenses that are thinner in the middle than at the edges are called concave lenses. A concave lens makes parallel rays of light spread out, or diverge, as they pass out of the lens.

Different colors of light are refracted by different amounts, which causes colored fringes to appear around the images of objects seen through a glass of water. The colors of the rainbow are also caused by the process of refraction.

See also: ELECTROMAGNETISM • LIGHT • RAINBOW • SPECTROSCOPY

Refrigeration

Refrigeration is an artificial coldness produced by the evaporation and condensation of fluid. Refrigeration is used in the home and in industry, especially for preserving food. At one time, the coldness used to keep food fresh at home came from a large slab of ice placed in the top of an icebox. Now, most refrigerators are powered by electricity.

In its simplest terms, refrigeration is the moving of heat from one place to another. The absence of heat is what creates the coldness, and removing more heat makes an enclosed space colder still.

Modern refrigeration systems rely on the fact that as a substance evaporates (becomes a gas), it absorbs heat. Evaporation is therefore used to remove heat and bring about the coldness inside a refrigerator.

The substance that evaporates is a chemical called a refrigerant. The refrigerant is a liquid under high pressure outside the refrigerator, but when it passes into an evaporator inside the refrigerator, it turns into a gas. As this happens, the refrigerant takes in heat from the refrigerator, and gradually the air in the compartment cools down. Then the refrigerant gas, carrying heat, passes into the condenser. It loses its heat through the condenser coils, which are outside the refrigerator, and becomes a liquid again. The cooled liquid refrigerant goes back through the evaporator, and the liquid-gas-liquid cycle is repeated.

Domestic refrigerators

Refrigerators in the home usually have two storage areas. The large main section keeps food fresh in cool air. The smaller compartment is kept at freezing temperatures and is used for freezing foods and for making ice cubes. The exterior of a refrigerator contains insulating material to keep out heat. The temperature inside a refrigerator is controlled by a thermostat, which regulates the rate of circulation of the refrigerant and thus the amount of cooling.

There are two types of domestic refrigeration systems: the compression system, which is the most common; and the absorption system, which is not as powerful.

◄ *Food is loaded into an industrial freezer. Many foods in supermarkets are delivered from many miles away, or are imported from abroad. Without refrigeration during transportation and storage, these foods would spoil before they arrived on the shelves.*

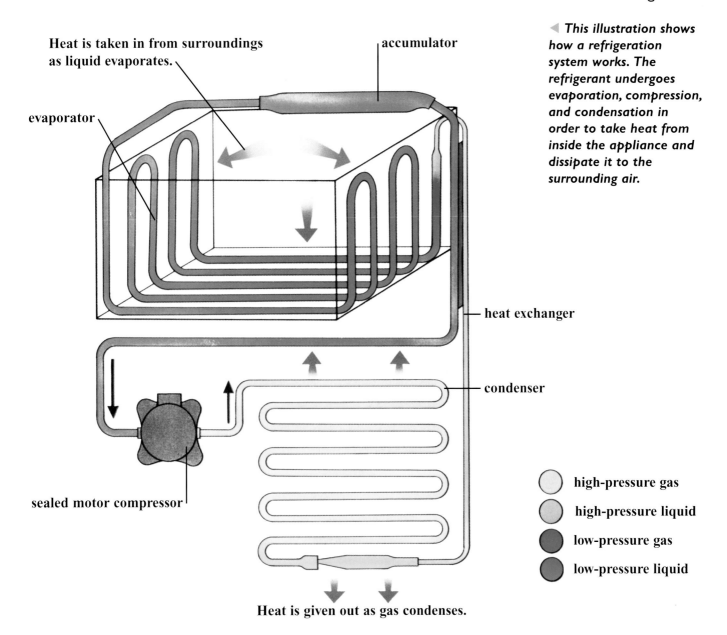

Heat is taken in from surroundings as liquid evaporates.

accumulator

evaporator

◀ *This illustration shows how a refrigeration system works. The refrigerant undergoes evaporation, compression, and condensation in order to take heat from inside the appliance and dissipate it to the surrounding air.*

heat exchanger

condenser

sealed motor compressor

high-pressure gas

high-pressure liquid

low-pressure gas

low-pressure liquid

Heat is given out as gas condenses.

The compression system

This system uses an electric motor to drive a compressor, which pumps the refrigerant through the system. The low pressure inlet side of the compressor is connected to the evaporator inside the refrigerator, while the high pressure outlet side is connected to a condenser.

When the refrigerant enters the compressor from the evaporator, it is a gas and is relatively warm. The compressor pressurizes the gas and passes it into the condenser, where it is cooled down and turns into its liquid form, losing heat in the process. The condenser is cooled by a fan, by water, or just by cooling fins, like a radiator.

The liquid refrigerant is then sucked into the evaporator by the low pressure side of the compressor. In the evaporator, the refrigerant expands, its pressure falls, and it turns back into a gas. As it does so, it takes in heat from the refrigerated area, thus cooling it down. The gas then passes back to the compressor, where it returns to its liquid state, and the cycle starts over again.

The absorption system

The absorption refrigeration system uses ammonia as the refrigerant. Ammonia liquor—a mixture of ammonia (NH_3) and water—is heated in a gas boiler. The ammonia boils off as a gas and passes to the condenser. As more ammonia turns to gas, the pressure in the condenser increases. When the pressure has built up so that it is high enough to turn the ammonia into a liquid, heat is given off.

The liquid ammonia then passes into the evaporator, which is inside the refrigerator. The pressure is reduced in the evaporator, and the liquid turns back into a gas, taking heat from the cold compartment and reducing the temperature inside it. After leaving the evaporator, the ammonia gas passes into an absorber, which is outside the refrigerated area.

The absorber contains weak ammonia liquor, which has circulated from the boiler. The ammonia gas is absorbed into the weak ammonia liquor, creating a low pressure in the evaporator. The liquor gradually becomes stronger as it takes in more and more ammonia. The strong liquor then returns to the boiler to continue the cycle.

The refrigerant

A number of fluids are suitable for use as refrigerants in compression systems. The most effective refrigerants, however, are a chemical group known as chlorofluorocarbons (CFCs) or Freons (their trade name). CFCs are based on carbon, chlorine, and fluorine. It has been discovered, though, that these gases could be damaging to Earth's ozone layer, so their use has been restricted. Replacement refrigerants have so far not proven to be as good.

Uses of refrigeration

Both absorption and compression systems are used in refrigerators for domestic and industrial use. The absorption system has the advantage that it is quieter than the compression system and can be constructed with no moving parts. However, the compression system is more powerful and is used for large deep-freeze units.

Refrigerated ships and road and rail vehicles carry fresh food all over the world. At their destination, the foods may be stored in large cold-storage warehouses, which use hundreds of tons of refrigerant and several compressor units. The storage area may be cooled by circulating refrigerant through pipes, by using the refrigerant to cool brine (saltwater), which is then circulated around the store in pipes, or by a cold-air circulation system.

Freezing is used in the food industry in a number of ways. Food may be deep frozen using a blast of very cold air. It may also be frozen between hollow metal plates in which the refrigerant passes, dipped in a refrigerated liquid such as brine, or sprayed with a very cold liquid, such as liquid nitrogen.

In freeze-drying, the food is first frozen. Any water in it is changed to ice. The food is then heated in a vacuum so that the ice changes directly to water vapor, leaving the food completely dry.

◀ *This modern household refrigerator contains a large cold compartment for fresh food, a freezer compartment, and an ice maker. The thick doors and sides contain insulation to keep out exterior heat.*

See also: FOOD TECHNOLOGY • THERMOSTAT

Relativity

The special and general theories of relativity proposed by Albert Einstein describe what happens to objects as they travel at speeds approaching the speed of light. Although it seems to go against common sense, Einstein found that time, length, and mass can change at extremely high speeds. Several of the strange results Einstein predicted have since proved to be true.

In the late nineteenth century, physicists were trying to explain the means by which light propagated through different materials such as air, glass, and a vacuum. They came up with a convenient answer called the ether, which was an unknown substance that filled the entire universe. The problem was that no one could detect the ether. Scientists predicted that as Earth travels around the Sun, its passage through the ether should generate a trail of wind behind it.

Measuring the ether

In 1887, U.S. physicists Albert Michelson (1852–1931) and Edward Morley (1838–1923) devised an experiment to detect the ether. They built a machine, called an interferometer, that splits a light beam in two and then brings the rays together. Michelson and Morley expected that the pattern of light and dark stripes produced by interference when the split light beam was brought together would change as the interferometer was rotated in the ether wind. They observed no change whatsoever.

Some scientists tried to explain these results and said that even though the ether could not be measured, it still existed. However, German-born U.S. physicist Albert Einstein (1879–1955) was not satisfied with this explanation.

Are you moving?

Imagine a bus driver sitting in stationary bus at a bus stop, watching another bus move away. Although the driver knows his or her bus is not

▼ Astronauts in space experience weightlessness as they free fall toward Earth relative to the spacecraft.

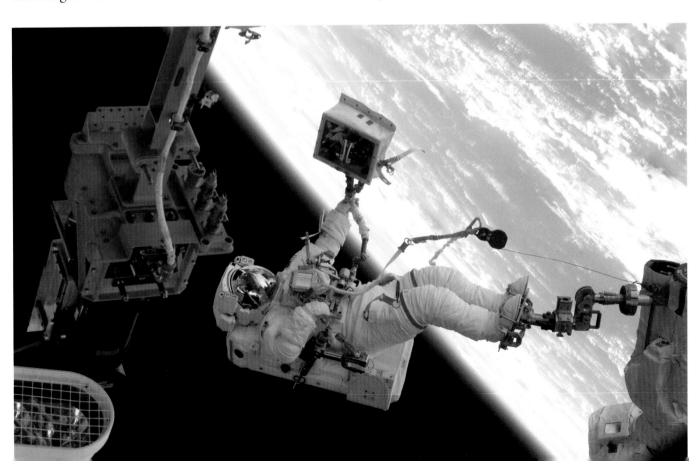

◀ **Einstein works through a problem in his study at Princeton, New Jersey, in 1951.**

light would depend on the relative motion of the observer and light source. Einstein said the speed of light would always be measured to have the same value, regardless of the motion of observer or source.

This may seem rather strange. After all, a person riding a bicycle knows that someone following in an automobile will always catch up with them if the automobile travels faster than the cyclist. However, this event does not happen at the speed of light. The speed of light is the fastest possible speed in the universe. Nothing can travel faster. So if a person tried to chase a pulse of light by traveling in an extremely fast rocket, she could never catch up with the pulse because she could never travel faster than the speed of the light pulse.

What happens next?

The principle of relativity seems very simple, but it causes some strange things to happen—although not in the everyday world, where events occur at very slow speeds compared to the speed of light. A person can walk at about 3 miles (5 kilometers) per hour, and an automobile can travel up to 200 miles

moving, he or she may feel as if it is moving backward. The same effect can be felt when someone is sitting in a train stopped at a station, watching another train move away from the platform. The passenger may feel that the train in which he or she is sitting is moving and that the moving train is standing still.

If the same passenger is sitting in a train that is moving at a constant speed, he or she may not realize the train is moving along—unless, of course, he or she looks out the window. The passenger could throw a ball up into the air and catch it in exactly the same way whether sitting on this train or standing still on the sidewalk.

Einstein realized that whether an experiment is conducted while standing still or while moving at a constant speed, the results will always be the same. This is called the principle of relativity, and it is fundamental to Einstein's special theory of relativity. Before Einstein, scientists thought that the speed of

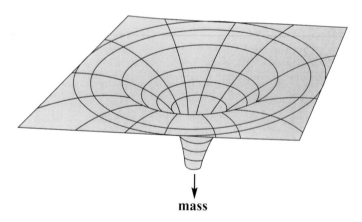

mass

▲ **Gravity is due to the effect that mass has on space-time. Imagine placing a heavy ball on the surface of a rubber sheet. The heavy ball creates a dip in the sheet into which a light ball would roll if it was placed on the edge of the sheet. The light ball moves toward the heavy ball, not because of an attractive force between the two objects, but because the mass of the heavy ball has distorted the space through which the light ball moves.**

(160 kilometers) per hour. The fastest rockets can travel at about 20 miles (32 kilometers) per second. Light travels at 186,000 miles (300,000 kilometers) per second. It is only when people consider the motion of objects at speeds approaching the speed of light that the strange effects of relativity start to become noticeable.

At these very high speeds, time and mass no longer obey the usual laws of physics. Some of what happens seems to go against common sense, but Einstein proved it all mathematically.

What time is it?

In everyday life, the passage of time is regular and even. Each second lasts as long as the one before it and as long as the one after it. At speeds approaching the speed of light, however, time does not pass so regularly. A clock traveling at half the speed of light would start to run slow. If a clock could travel at exactly the same speed as light, it would stop altogether.

▼ *Light curves toward a massive body as it travels past. For example, the Sun bends light from a distant star, changing the star's apparent position. Starlight in the direction of the Sun can be seen during a solar eclipse, when the glare from the sunlight is blocked.*

This part of Einstein's theory, called time dilation, has been tested by scientists at the European Center for Nuclear Research (CERN) in Switzerland. The scientists made tiny particles, called muons, travel through a particle accelerator. Muons are short-lived particles and usually decay (break down) after about two-millionths of a second. When the scientists at CERN made the muons travel around at speeds approaching the speed of light, they found that the muons took much longer to decay.

The same thing would happen if a train could be made to travel past a standing train at a speed approaching the speed of light. The passengers on the standing train would see a clock on the moving train run slow, and passengers on the moving train would see a clock run slow on the stationary train.

How long is it? How heavy?

As an object approaches the incredibly fast speed of light, it would appear to become shorter and shorter. To the observers on the moving train, the standing train would shrink. To the observers on the stationary train, the moving train would appear to shrink. If an observer could measure the weight of the moving train as it approached the speed of light, he or she would find that it became heavier

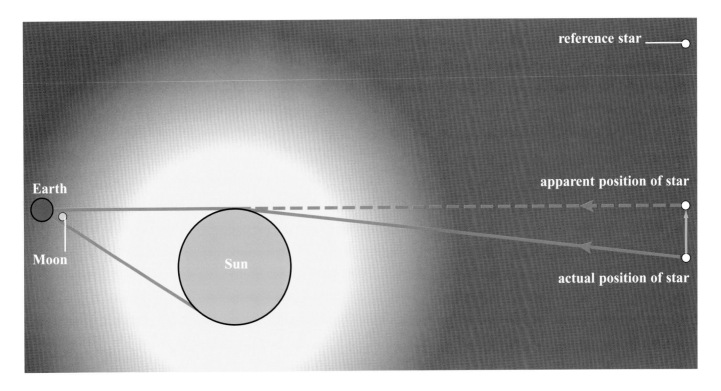

reference star

Earth

Moon

Sun

apparent position of star

actual position of star

◀ *The enormous gravity of a supermassive black hole tears apart a star (colored orange). A tiny fraction of the doomed star's mass (the white stream encircling the black hole) is consumed by the black hole. The rest is flung away into space (the red mist).*

and heavier the faster it traveled. It could never actually reach the speed of light, because then it would become infinitely heavy. The effect of an increase in mass has been checked in experiments involving subatomic particles. This increase in mass and change in length led Einstein to his famous equation, which relates energy (*E*) and mass (*m*):

$$E = mc^2$$

where *c* is the speed of light.

General relativity

The special theory of relativity, first published in 1905, applied only to objects moving at constant speed. Einstein then extended his theory to describe the motion of objects in acceleration (speeding up). His work culminated in the general theory of relativity, which was published in 1916.

Einstein realized that, in a small laboratory where the force of gravity is always the same, it is impossible to tell the difference between the effects of gravity and acceleration. Put simply, acceleration and gravity are one and the same. An astronaut in a rocket cannot tell whether the rocket is at rest on Earth or accelerating at 31.5 feet (9.81 meters) per second squared. In both situations, the astronaut's feet are pressed against the floor with the same force. Einstein called this the principle of equivalence. From this principle, Einstein concluded that gravity is not a force of attraction that pulls objects together. Rather, it is a result of space and time being curved by mass.

Many of the great mysteries of the universe have been made much clearer using the general theory of relativity. One prediction of Einstein's theory is the existence of extremely dense celestial objects called black holes. The gravity inside a black hole is so great that nothing—not even light itself—can escape from it, so it is impossible to see one directly. General relativity has also been used to support the big bang theory of the origin of the universe, since it predicts that the universe is expanding.

See also: BLACK HOLE • EINSTEIN, ALBERT • GRAVITY • MOTION • ORBIT • PARTICLE PHYSICS • PHYSICS • TIME • UNIVERSE

Relay

A relay is a switch that makes or breaks contacts in an electrical circuit. Relays can be worked by a simple magnet or by an electromagnet—iron that has been magnetized by an electrical current. A relay passes action from one electrical circuit to another, in order to control it, and is often used in remote control devices.

A magnetic relay is operated by a simple magnet. Most relays, however, are operated by an electromagnetic system. An electrical current from a control circuit is passed through a coil of wire wound around an iron core. This sets up a magnetic field, which affects a part of the device called an armature. This strip of iron, controlled by the electromagnetic force, makes or breaks the electrical contacts in the operating circuit.

The control current

A relay is a simple device, but designing a relay system is not always that easy. Many things must be taken into account, for example, the type of current passing through the coil.

Electrical current is passed through a circuit in one of two possible ways. With a direct current (DC), the electricity flows steadily in one direction. With an alternating current (AC), the electricity flows in opposite directions at regular intervals.

When current is passed through the relay coil, a flux pattern is set up around the coil. This is a pattern of magnetic flow, which affects the iron armature. The armature always moves in the direction of least resistance (reluctance) to the magnetic lines of force, and this will be the same whether the current is DC or AC.

▶ *Electromagnetic relays are used to control a high voltage current with low voltage signals.*

Contacts

The materials used to make relay contacts are very important. When the voltage is high, for example, sparks can damage the surface of the contacts and cause them to stick together. With low voltages, there is greater resistance between the contacts.

Another problem is caused by bounce. This effect occurs when the electrical contacts make and break several times before settling down. It is a problem that often occurs when the electromagnetic relay is being used with electronic circuits that operate at very high speeds. Bounce is a potential problem with an AC control current. Between each change of direction in the current, there is a split second when there is no current at all. If the contacts were rigid, they would be bouncing continually. Instead, they are made of springy metal and are held in contact under tension.

Contacts can be arranged in all kinds of ways, depending on the way in which the circuit is to be operated. The relays in a telephone exchange can operate up to six sets each. Contacts are usually made of copper, but silver, gold, and mercury are sometimes used. With mercury contacts, two electrodes are sealed with some mercury in a glass

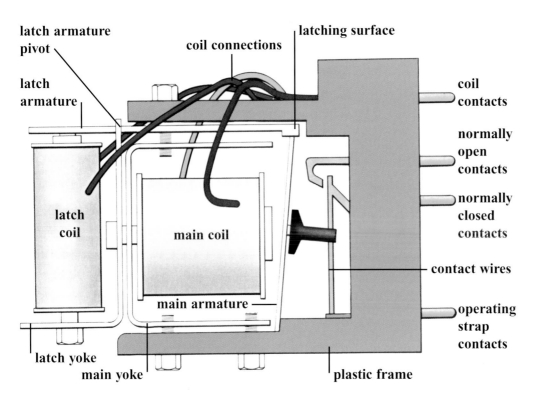

latch armature pivot

latch armature

coil connections

latching surface

latch coil

main coil

latch
main armature

latch yoke

main yoke

plastic frame

coil contacts

normally open contacts

normally closed contacts

contact wires

operating strap contacts

◀ *In this latching relay only pulses of current are needed to change contacts. A pulse through the main coil sets off the main armature, which locks under the latch armature. A pulse through the latch coil makes the latch armature pivot to release the main armature. The contacts then return to their normal positions.*

case, which is joined to the armature. When this moves, the mercury surrounds the two electrodes and conducts electricity across the gap.

Relay designs

In a normal relay design, the armature moves on a pivot, with a separate return spring. It is made of metal that is magnetically soft—that is, a metal that does not stay magnetized once the coil has been switched off.

Relays are normally operated by the control current being switched on or off. Sometimes, however, it is useful to operate the relay by using

pulses of current. In this case, a second coil and armature are brought in to control the action of the first. This is called a latching relay.

Reed relays have a very different design. In these relays, the armature and the contacts are combined. Two strips of metal are put inside a glass tube filled with nitrogen gas. They are made of chrome-iron alloy (magnetically soft), and the contact points are alloyed with gold to avoid resistance.

A coil wrapped around the glass tube creates a magnetic field, which forces the contacts together. The reed relay can work millions of times without fault. It is fast and uses less power.

Other types of relays

Not all relays are magnetic or electromagnetic. For example, contacts in a thermostat system are made when a strip of two different metals (a bimetallic strip) is affected by temperature. Also, the job of the electromagnetic relay is often taken over now by new electronic technology.

▼ *In this reed relay, current flowing through the electromagnet forces the contacts inside the glass tube together.*

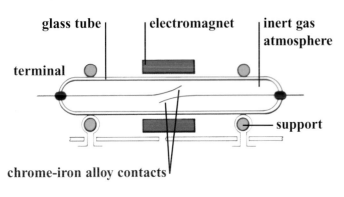

glass tube

electromagnet

inert gas atmosphere

terminal

support

chrome-iron alloy contacts

See also: ALLOY • ELECTRICITY • ELECTROMAGNETISM • MAGNETISM • RESISTANCE • SEMICONDUCTOR

Remote control

Remote control is the control of something from a distance. Remote-control systems sometimes use extended, physical control links, but more usually use radio waves or other forms of wireless connection. Remote-control systems have numerous applications, from operating television sets to controlling space probes.

Remote control is used in the home, in science, and in industry. All remote-control systems involve the control of an object or device in one place from another place some distance away. The objects controlled and the methods vary widely. Four important types of remote-control systems are: radio control, infrared remote control, remote-handling equipment, and telemetry.

RADIO CONTROL

Radio control is a common form of remote control. It is a way of directing the movements of one or more objects by radio waves from some distance away. A remote-controlled model airplane is a good example. The airplane can be made to take off and land, go faster and slow down, turn and bank—all directed from the ground-based operator.

Radio-control equipment can be divided into two types: single-channel and multichannel. The difference between the two types is that single-channel equipment can control only one function, such as steering, whereas a multichannel system can control several functions.

Single-channel radio control

Equipment for single-channel radio control consists of a transmitter (sending device), a relay (a device that responds to small electrical signals by activating switches in an electric circuit), and an electro-mechanical device called an actuator or escapement, which controls the single function.

When the lever, button, or "keying switch" on the transmitter is moved, a constant-frequency radio signal is emitted. This signal is picked up and amplified (strengthened) by the receiver in the model airplane, for example. The amplified signal operates the relay, which in turn operates the actuator. The actuator may be connected, for example, to the airplane's rudder by a crank. Because a single-channel radio-control system is fairly simple, the mechanics can only move in 90-degree turns. The result is a left-neutral-right-neutral-left sequence.

▲ A child uses a simple remote-control device to direct the movements of a toy truck. Radio signals from the handset allow the child to steer the truck and make it speed up or slow down.

◀ *Home entertainment equipment can usually be controlled using handheld remote-control devices. These devices work by sending coded pulses of infrared light to a receiver on the equipment.*

The single-channel system is limited because it can only operate one function—such as the throttle for speed or the brakes for slowing down—by turning it on or off. It cannot pause in any intermediate position.

Multichannel radio control

The first examples of multichannel radio-control systems were large and heavy and not always very reliable. These systems used tone transmitters that could produce up to 12 different tones. Each tone would make one of 12 reed switches in the receiver vibrate and close a contact. As specific contacts closed, they would make a device called a servomechanism (servo for short) produce the required movement.

Modern multichannel radio-control equipment uses digital pulsing systems. These systems are more reliable than tone transmitters and allow finer control. The lever on a digital-pulsing transmitter can be operated in the same way as the real control column of an airplane. When moved, even slightly, it causes a proportional movement in the body of the airplane.

The transmitter produces a series of pulses all the time it is switched on. A group of pulses contains one more pulses than the number of channels (controllable functions on the model). The "spaces" between each pulse are read as pulses by the receiver. The signal containing the pulses is amplified by the receiver and passed on to a decoder.

The decoder sends the spaces to the appropriate servo, which then generates another pulse of the same length but opposite polarity (either positive or negative). These immediately cancel each other out, and the motor does not operate.

If a lever on the transmitter is operated, however, it causes the corresponding space to change in duration (length). Arriving at the servo, this space (pulse) no longer matches the one produced by the servo. Thus, the two no longer cancel each other out, the motor starts, and the function is operated.

As soon as the motor starts, the servo pulse is changed. When it matches the transmitted pulse, the two cancel each other out, and the motor stops. When the lever is returned to neutral, the servo does the same. One or all of the levers on the transmitter can be operated at the same time.

INFRARED REMOTE CONTROL

The most familiar type of remote control is infrared remote control, which is widely used in the home for operating electronic entertainment systems and other equipment.

Infrared remote control uses pulses of invisible, infrared light to send control signals to a device. Unlike radio transmitters, infrared transmitters have to be able to directly, or indirectly, "see" the device they are operating. For example, infrared signals can reflect off, but not pass through, walls.

When a button is pressed on an infrared remote-control handset, it completes a specific connection. A microchip in the handset then produces a signal that relates to that button. Transistors amplify this signal and send it to a light-emitting diode (LED) on the front of the handset, which translates the signal into infrared light. An infrared sensor on the device being operated then detects the light signal and prompts the device to react appropriately.

REMOTE HANDLING

Sometimes people have to work with objects or substances that are too dangerous to handle directly. This is true of radioactive materials, for example. Remote handling is a form of remote control that lets people work with such materials while keeping them at a safe distance.

Remote-handling devices are needed for work such as mixing radioactive liquids and conducting tests with radioactive materials. This is necessary because radioactivity can be very harmful to humans.

The simplest remote handlers are mechanical tools rather than electrical devices. These tools, called long-reachers, are often tongs on a long handle, which can reach to about 9 feet (3 meters). The end of the handle has a hand grip connected to the tongs by a wire. The operator can make the tongs open and shut to grasp and move objects. Some long-reachers are also able to rotate or tilt the tongs, but they still cannot do much more than move containers around.

A more complicated kind of remote handler is one that can be used through a protective wall. In this case, the remote-handling device consists of straight rods put through the wall on ball-and-

▼ *This X-36 experimental pilotless aircraft is on a test flight at Edwards Air Force Base in California. The aircraft contains highly advanced remote-control systems, and it is remotely flown from the ground.*

Remote control

▶ *This remote-controlled military robot is being used to examine a suspicious package during a counter-terrorism exercise. Remote-control machines allow dangerous operations to be carried out from a distance without endangering the lives of human operators.*

socket joints, which allow turning of the rods in all directions. Various tools are attached to the rods, and these are operated by a pistol grip at the outside end. The operator can cut, file, shake, and drill objects as well as simply move them. Operators can see what they are doing by looking through lead glass windows.

The most complicated remote-handling devices are called master-slave manipulators. The operator is the master, and the tool heads are the slaves. More than any other kind of remote handler, the master-slave manipulator can do exactly what the operator wants. It is really like having an extra pair of arms and hands on the other side of the protective wall.

One model of a master-slave manipulator has a telescopic arm hung from a pivoted (rotating) joint over the working area. Many different kinds of tools can be attached to the arm—power tools as well as hand tools. Operators use two rods connected to the telescopic arm to work the slave tool. They can do very complicated work with almost as much control as having the objects in their own hands.

TELEMETRY

Telemetry is the process of sending or exchanging data by wire or radio to another device some distance away. Telemetry has made it possible to receive scientific information from space probes sent to outer reaches of the solar system and to control and reprogram them from afar.

Although some telemetry devices move, such as those on satellites, most are in fixed locations. They are used to take measurements automatically, such as the size of an electrical voltage, air or water pressure, or temperature. The results are sent by direct wire or radio link to a receiving station that may be anything from a few feet to thousands of miles away.

A basic telemetry system consists of a primary detector (called a pickup), a transmission system, a receiving system, and an output device. The output device may display or record the data or do both. The details of designs for telemetry equipment vary according to their purpose.

Early telemetry systems

One of the first patents for telemetry equipment in the United States was issued in 1885. The first telemetry systems were used by electricity supply companies for measuring the voltages and currents of the electricity used throughout their distribution networks. Electrical information from telemetry pickups was sent down direct landline wires, called pilot lines, to electricity control rooms. After World War I (1914–1918), the signals were transmitted along the power lines themselves.

Electrical telemetry

One form of telemetry is electrical telemetry. A simple form of electrical telemetry is often used in fixed remote-metering systems, such as those first used by electricity supply companies to check their power supplies. The pickups, such as voltmeters and ammeters, are connected by individual wires to central control rooms where all the measurements are collated. This system makes it easy to keep a constant check on what is happening throughout the electricity distribution network.

Simple electrical telemetry systems work well for short distances where only a small number of individual measurements is needed. Because each pickup needs its own circuit, however, it is very expensive to provide a large number of circuits over a long distance.

Another form of electrical telemetry uses instruments that produce electrical pulses. Instead of transmitting an electrical signal directly as it is produced by a pickup, the signal is converted into coded pulses. The speed of these pulses is in ratio to the quantity being measured by the pickup. The pulses are sent to the receiving instruments, which then decode the impulses to show the measurement. This is called pulse-rate telemetry.

A variation of the same idea is pulse-length telemetry. In this case, the length of the pulse, rather than the rate at which it is transmitted, is in proportion to the measurement.

▼ *This image shows the space probe* **Viking II** *on Mars. Telemetry systems enabled the probe to send back data from its onboard scientific sensors to the control center on Earth.*

◀ **This is the European Space Operations Centre, which is the hub of numerous telemetry systems that connect European spacecraft with Earth.**

Frequency modulation (FM) is often used to change the radio signals, and the carrier signal may be modulated by a group of subcarriers, each of which is of a different frequency.

Practical uses

Telemetry has many practical and scientific uses in the modern world. Besides its long-standing use in monitoring electricity supplies, it is also used in other supply systems, such as gas, oil, and water pipelines. Flow rates and pressures can be monitored all along the lines by signals coming from a small number of telemetry stations.

A combination of different types of multiplexing and different forms of signal modulation is used in highly developed equipment to produce radio-telemetry links for special purposes, such as missile monitoring and control systems.

One of the most important uses of telemetry is the sending of data to and from satellites, space probes, and piloted space vehicles. Automatic systems used by piloted spacecraft send and receive data concerning course position and engineering systems, as well as transmitting information about astronauts' breathing and pulse rates.

Satellites, space probes, and other spacecraft transmit data covering a wide range of subjects, depending on the function of the craft. Aside from the pickups that monitor the onboard systems (such as the power supply) of the vehicles themselves, satellites and space probes carry instruments to collect information on, for example, radiation, magnetic fields, and Earth resources. This information is sent back through radio-telemetry links to tracking stations on the ground. Using these telemetry links, ground stations also control and reprogram the spacecraft.

Multiplex telemetry

Multiplex telemetry is an advanced form of telemetry that allows many different measurements or data signals to be sent over a single circuit, thus saving expensive circuitry. To make this system work, however, the signals must be kept separate. This process is called multiplexing. There are several different multiplex-telemetry systems.

A time-division multiplexing system scans each signal to be sent in a set order and transmits them in that order to the receiving station. The receiver scans the incoming signals and sends each set of pulses to the correct indicator or recording instrument. Both the transmitting and receiving ends of the system are operated at exactly the same time by a special pulse that acts as a signal before each scanning cycle. Time-division multiplexing systems may use either a pulse-rate system or a pulse-length system.

Radio telemetry

Telemetry signals may be carried by radio links as well as by wires. Radio signals are modulated, that is, varied by a subcarrier signal that carries the data. The subcarrier may either be a single data channel, or it may be time-division multiplexed.

See also: MICROWAVE RADIATION • RADIO • RADIOACTIVITY • REMOTE SENSOR • ROBOTICS • SATELLITE • SERVOMECHANISM • SPACE PROBE

Remote sensor

Remote sensors are devices that can locate people or animals by picking up sound, movement, or heat. Remote sensors also include airborne or space-based equipment used to analyze Earth's surface from afar.

The use of remote sensors has become particularly widespread since the development of microelectronics, which has enabled devices to become increasingly smaller and sophisticated. Remote sensors provide scientists with valuable information about animal movements and behavior. Military sensors, often called "bugs," help detect and monitor enemy troop movements. Remote sensors have also revolutionized archaeology, making it easier to identify archaeological sites.

Remote animal tracking

Remote sensors are particularly suitable for studying wild animals, as they cannot be studied easily from close up. Often the animal to be studied is caught by firing a drug-containing dart from a rifle. The drug makes the animal unconscious long enough for researchers to attach the tag or collar containing the sensor. The movement of tigers, wolves, and polar bears have all been followed in this way. Other remote sensors are not attached to animals directly but are planted in particular areas frequented by the study animals.

Wildlife biologists often use remote sensors in animal management. For example, by collaring some of a game population with radio transmitters, scientists can decide hunting quotas by tracking the animals' ranges—a sign of the population's success.

Military sensors

There are two chief types of military sensors—those that are dropped by airplane and those that are planted at ground level. Some of these devices pick up

▲ *This seal is being tagged by scientists so that they can monitor its movements. These remote sensors enable scientists to gain a better understanding of many animals that would otherwise be difficult to observe.*

seismic signals—that is, vibrations in the ground that might be caused by the stamping of marching feet. Others are sensitive to magnetic signals, sound, temperature, or even smell.

The signals are received by a computer, either on land or in an airplane. They are decoded, and the information is analyzed so that it can be used to plan the next strike against the enemy.

Air-delivered sensors

The best known sensor device dropped by airplane is the air-delivered seismic instrument device (ADSID). It is shaped like a small rocket, but it has large flights (tail wings like those on a dart) and a strange-looking set of prongs coming out of the tail.

signal to pick up, the device switches itself off to save the battery. Some UGSs are buried by an army patrol and recovered later at the end of the operation. Others, as with air-delivered devices, have a fixed life span. In these devices, when the battery runs down, it burns out the sensor's electronic circuitry, so that it cannot then be inspected by the enemy.

Remote sensors in archaeology

In the science of archaeology, remote sensing devices are those that see beyond what human eyes can see. A camera attached to an unmanned balloon was the first remote sensing instrument used by an archaeologist. Eventually, aerial photography came to be used to find and study archaeological sites all over the world. It was enhanced in the 1940s by infrared photography. Infrared photography detects infrared radiation, which is part of the electromagnetic spectrum that exists beyond visible light. The amount of infrared radiation detected depends on the heat given off (emitted) by an object. When used in aerial photography, infrared photography can highlight significant distinctions between ground surfaces and underground structures not detected in ordinary photographs.

Today's sophisticated geological remote sensors work from space shuttles, high-flying airplanes, and satellites. They are advanced types of radar that "see" below Earth's surface. The information they record is converted by computer into photographic images. They have revealed ancient roadways in Costa Rica, Mayan canal systems below thick jungle in Guatemala, and ancient riverbeds under the Sahara Desert. Remote sensors enable archaeologists to find, map, and study places where people lived in the past much faster and more efficiently than with many traditional field-based techniques.

When it lands, the ADSID nose-dives straight down into the ground, leaving the prongs showing above ground. The prongs are the antennas that pick up the seismic signals. They are painted green and shaped as they are for camouflage, so that they look like just another forest plant. The flights keep the device upright as it moves through the air and as it enters the ground.

Sensors planted by hand

Sensors dropped from planes can cover large areas, but they are less accurate than sensors planted by hand. These are usually known by the initials UGS, standing for unattended ground sensor. UGSs are often smaller than air-delivered sensors, and their antennas are shorter and thinner since they do not have to survive the shock of falling to Earth from an airplane. However, the range over which UGSs transmit is also shorter.

UGSs are powered by a built-in battery that can last for as long as 60 or 80 days, depending on how often the device is transmitting. When there is no

---

See also: MAGNETISM

Reproductive system

The human reproductive system contains specialized organs that bring genes from each parent together and combine them to form a new and unique set of genes. These genes then control the development of the fetus inside a woman's uterus.

The reproductive system is the part of the body that is used to produce offspring. A child develops according to a set of instructions called genes. Every cell of the human body carries two sets of genes, one set from each of its parents. The reproductive system brings these two half-sets of genes together to make a full set in a process called sexual reproduction.

A person's reproductive system produces sex cells, or gametes. The gametes are different from all other cells in the body because they have just one set of genes instead of the usual two sets. Female gametes are called ova (*singular*, ovum), or eggs. Male gametes are called sperm—tiny swimming cells that are pushed along by a tail-like structure called a flagellum.

A sperm cell swims to the egg and then fuses with it. This process is called fertilization. The genes in the sperm combine with the genes in the egg to make a double set. The new cell produced is called a zygote. This is the first cell of a new individual. The zygote begins to divide, forming a ball of identical cells. This process, and all of the child's future development, is driven by the genes inherited from his or her parents. Because half the genes come from the father and half from the mother, the child will have some characteristics of both parents.

For sexual reproduction to take place, animals must find a way of getting the sperm to an egg. Many aquatic animals simply release sperm or eggs into the water. This is called external fertilization.

▲ The reproductive systems of men and women are intimately involved in sexual intercourse. Sexual intercourse is a natural part of a loving relationship.

However, this can be wasteful and is difficult on land, so many animals, including humans and all other mammals, fertilize eggs internally in an intimate process called sexual intercourse. The male sex organs deliver the sperm directly to the egg. Many female animals lay eggs, and the developing embryo therefore develops outside the mother's body. However, most female mammals carry and nurture their young inside their reproductive system.

Female reproductive system

In the human reproductive system, sperm and eggs form inside structures called gonads. Female gonads are called ovaries. There are two ovaries, one on either side of the lower abdomen. When a girl is born, her ovaries already contain all the egg cells she will ever have. Other cells, called follicles,

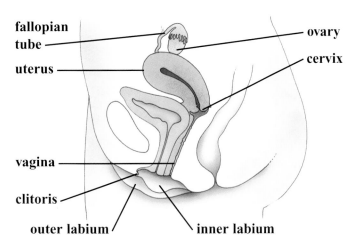

▲ *This illustration shows the main parts of the female reproductive system.*

surround the eggs and supply them with nutrients. The development of the eggs proceeds until the baby girl is born and then stops. When the girl reaches the age of 12 or 13 (a time called puberty), the eggs begin to develop again. Roughly once a month, one egg bursts out of the ovary. Triggered by hormones, this process is called ovulation. Without it, fertilization cannot occur. Ovulation continues until around the age of 45, when eggs stop being released. This stage is called menopause.

After leaving the ovary, an egg passes into a duct called a fallopian tube, where fertilization takes place. The two fallopian tubes (one from each

ovary) lead to a pear-shaped sac called the uterus. It is in this sac, which can swell to the size of a basketball, that a fetus develops during pregnancy.

At its base, the uterus narrows into a neck known as the cervix. This leads into a muscular tube, called the vagina. The vagina leads to the outside and provides the route through which a baby is born. Two folds of skin, the labia (*singular,* labium), protect the entrance to the vagina. Just above the entrance is the clitoris. Packed with nerve endings, the clitoris is a source of pleasure during sex.

Male reproductive system

Male gonads are called testes. Sperm develop best at temperatures lower than the rest of the body, so they lie outside the body in a sac called the scrotum.

Sperm production begins when a boy reaches puberty, usually around the age of 11 or 12, and it continues for the rest of his life. Sperm are produced inside tubes, called seminiferous tubules, in the testes (*singular,* testis). The sperm pass into a coiled tube called the epididymis, which arches around the top of each testis. There, the sperm complete their development. A long tube, called the vas deferens, carries sperm from each testis over the bladder and then merges with the urethra, which is a duct that carries urine from the bladder. The urethra leaves the man's body through the penis. As

DID YOU KNOW?

There is no bone inside the human penis. During sexual intercourse, it gets all the support it needs from the pressure of blood inside it. However, the penises of many other mammals, including some other primates, contain a bone called a bacula. Unlike almost all other bones, the bacula does not connect with other bones or muscles. Biologists are unsure what function the bacula provides. It may serve to increase the fluid pressure inside the penis, providing greater stiffness, or it may help trigger ovulation.

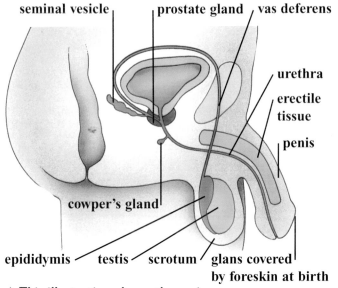

▲ *This illustration shows the main parts of the male reproductive system.*

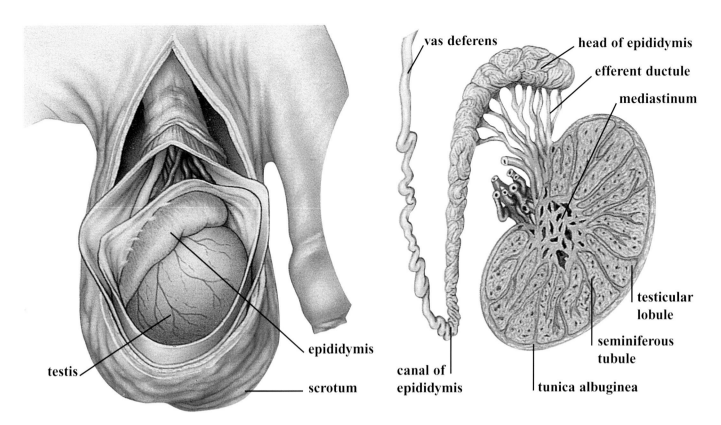

vas deferens

head of epididymis

efferent ductule

mediastinum

testicular lobule

seminiferous tubule

canal of epididymis

tunica albuginea

testis

epididymis

scrotum

▲ *The testes, or male sex organs, are held inside the scrotum. This is a loose sac that is positioned beneath the penis. The sperm produced by the testes is stored in the epididymis at the back of the scrotum before it passes through tubes to the penis during sex.*

well as passing urine, the penis is used for depositing sperm close to the woman's egg during sexual intercourse.

What is sexual intercourse?

For fertilization to occur, the woman must be at the right stage of her menstrual cycle. In other words, an egg needs to be in one of the fallopian tubes. During sex, each partner becomes sexually aroused.

Before arousal, a man's penis is soft. It is not supported by bones as are most other parts of the body. The penis needs to enter the vagina to deposit sperm, but it needs to become much firmer to do this. During arousal, blood collects inside the penis, and this makes the penis swell up, stiffen, and point upward. This is called an erection.

During intercourse, the man puts his penis inside the woman's vagina and moves it in and out. This increases the arousal of both partners. Eventually,

the man reaches a point where muscular contractions force sperm through the penis. This is called ejaculation. During ejaculation, glands under the bladder add secretions to the sperm, forming a liquid called semen. The sperm swim through the semen, which also contains the nutrients they need.

DID YOU KNOW?

Men and women differ in other ways besides the main sex organs. For example, although both boys and girls are born with nipples and mammary glands, it is only in girls that they enlarge to become distinct breasts and active milk-secreting organs after childbirth. Women have broader hips, reflecting a pelvic opening large enough for childbirth. Men have facial hair, bigger muscles, and deep voices. Both sexes have hair around their genitals. Such features are called secondary sexual characteristics, which appear during puberty in response to the release of sex hormones.

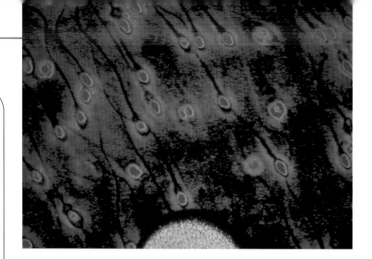

▲ *The semen released from the penis is filled with sperm. These swim into the woman's uterus, and one merges with an egg in a process called fertilization.*

this far—the hostile environment of the female reproductive tract allows only the strongest sperm to reach the egg.

Those that successfully reach their destination crowd around the egg. Each sperm releases proteins called enzymes that eat away at the gel-like outer layer of the egg. Once a single sperm has penetrated this layer, the cell membrane of the egg changes its structure. It releases granules that swell up, pushing the rest of the sperm away and ensuring that just one succeeds in fertilizing the egg.

Implantation and pregnancy

The fertilized egg is now called a zygote. Filled with all the genetic information it needs, the zygote divides rapidly to make more cells. Hairlike filaments, called cilia, in the walls of the fallopian tube waft the zygote down toward the uterus. Hormones released by the ovary trigger the uterus wall to become thicker. If the egg remains unfertilized, the uterus lining breaks down and leaves the body through the vagina in a process called menstruation. If the egg has formed a zygote, it embeds in the uterus wall. This occurs about six days after fertilization. By this stage, the zygote consists of about 130 cells. It releases chemicals that alert the body that pregnancy has begun. After nine months of further development, the baby is ready to leave the uterus during the birthing process.

Up to 200 million sperm may be released during a single ejaculation. Ejaculation occurs at the peak of sexual excitement, called an orgasm. Women experience orgasm in a different way. The vaginal wall contracts to draw sperm deeper inside. The sperm swim through the cervix toward the egg.

The journey to the egg

After ejaculation, millions of sperm enter the vagina, but most are doomed to die. Sperm follow chemicals released by the egg in the fallopian tube. The female reproductive tract can be a hostile environment for sperm. They must swim through mucus at the cervix and then travel along the wall of the uterus. The mucus at the cervix and inside the uterus becomes thinner and easier for sperm to swim through when an egg is ready for fertilization. However, fewer than one thousand sperm reach the fallopian tube. Poor-quality sperm do not make it

See also: PREGNANCY AND BIRTH

Resistance

When a person wades through water, the water slows his or her movement. In physics, resistance means the power of a body that acts in opposition to the pressure of another body.

When people talk about resistance, they are often referring to electrical resistance. However, materials can also resist a magnetic field (called magnetic resistance) or a pushing force. Liquids and gases can resist flowing.

Electrical resistance

If a battery is put in a flashlight and the switch turned on, the bulb illuminates. A current is passing through the bulb's filament. The current is produced by electrons moving through the filament. However, the movement of the electrons through the filament is slowed down because the metal atoms that make up the filament get in the way, resisting the flow of electrons. This is called electrical resistance. Electrical resistance causes materials to heat up. In a filament, the heat produced by electrical resistance can be seen as light.

Materials that make it difficult for electrons to pass through them have a high electrical resistance. Other materials that make it easy for the electrons to pass through have a low electrical resistance.

Conductors and insulators

Any material that allows electrical current to pass through it is called a conductor. Metals are good conductors of electricity. When some conductors become very cold, they can lose all their resistance. This characteristic is called superconductivity. Superconductors are used to make very powerful magnets.

Some materials have a very high resistance to the flow of an electrical current. They are called insulators. Plastic and rubber are good insulators.

▲ *Electrical wires are made from metals that have low electrical resistance. The insulation around the wires has a high resistance to protect people from shocks.*

Somewhere between conductors and insulators is a group of materials called semiconductors. They include silicon and germanium.

The important property of semiconductors is that their electrical resistance can be made to change. When a semiconductor is exposed to light or heat, its resistance goes down. The resistance of a semiconductor can also be made to fall if tiny impurities of another substance are added to it. Semiconductors are very important in modern electronics, as they are used to make silicon chips.

Magnetic resistance

Some materials are easily magnetized. They have a low magnetic resistance. Other materials have a high magnetic resistance and are not easily magnetized. When a material is magnetized, it can be thought of as having lines of magnetic force, known as flux, passing through it.

◀ *In this photograph, roller bearings are being manufactured. Bearings are used to reduce frictional resistance, and thus wear, between moving mechanical parts.*

Materials can become magnetized either by an electrical field or by another magnetic field. The magnetic resistance, also called the reluctance, is affected by the strength of the field that is producing the magnetism and also by the amount of flux produced.

Friction

If a person tries to slide two rough objects over each other, he or she will have to push them hard to make them slide. The resistance that must be overcome is the force of friction. Even very smooth surfaces touching each other will have some friction between them if they are pushed, because all objects have surfaces that are irregular or bumpy to some degree. Glass or polished metal may look smooth, but on a microscopic scale, their surfaces appear uneven. These uneven parts get locked together and produce friction.

Even air sliding over an automobile or airplane can produce friction called drag. Automobiles and aircraft are specially designed to reduce drag. Reducing the drag means that vehicles need less fuel—or energy—to overcome the forces holding them back.

Viscosity

Molasses is a viscous liquid. It does not flow very easily. The forces of friction inside the molasses resist its motion, giving it a high viscosity. Liquids that flow easily, such as water, have a low viscosity. Gases also have some viscosity, although less than the viscosity of liquids.

The frictional forces inside a liquid come from the molecules of the liquid holding it together. They try to resist any outside force. When a liquid is heated, the energy of the molecules increases, and the force holding the molecules together weakens. So liquids become less viscous as they are heated.

Gases are different. The viscosity of gas comes from the movement of the gas molecules. As gas is heated, the molecules move around more quickly, so the viscosity of a gas increases as it is heated.

The frictional forces inside liquids are much less than the forces of friction between two solids, so liquids can help to reduce friction between two solid surfaces. This process is called lubrication.

> *See also:* INSULATOR • LUBRICATION • SEMICONDUCTOR • SUPERCONDUCTIVITY

Resistor

Resistors are electrical devices that impede the passage of an electrical current in a circuit. Resistors can be found in almost every item that uses electricity, from computers and color televisions to radios and refrigerators.

When an electrical current flows through a conductor, such as a metal wire, an electric potential, or voltage, exists between the two ends of the wire. This electric potential drives negatively charged particles called electrons from the negative end of the conductor to the positive end of the conductor. As these electrons move through the conductor, they collide with the atoms that make up the conductor. It is these collisions that create the property of electrical resistance.

Resistance is the ratio of the electric potential (in volts) to the current that flows (in amps). It is measured in units called ohms. For most substances, the ratio is constant for all voltages. For others, it changes as the voltage changes, and these substances are called semiconductors.

How easily electrons pass through a substance is a measure of the resistivity of that substance. Every material has a unique resistivity value. A material with a high resistivity value is called an insulator; one with a low resistivity value is called a conductor. The resistivity value of a semiconductor falls between that of a conductor and an insulator.

Another important property of a resistor is the power rating, which is measured in units called watts. When electrons collide with the atoms of the

▼ *When these resistors are connected in a circuit, each one offers a fixed resistance to the passage of the electrical current flowing through the circuit.*

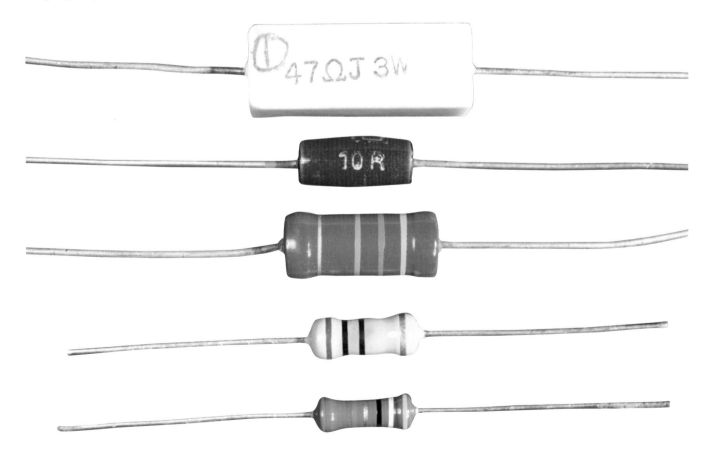

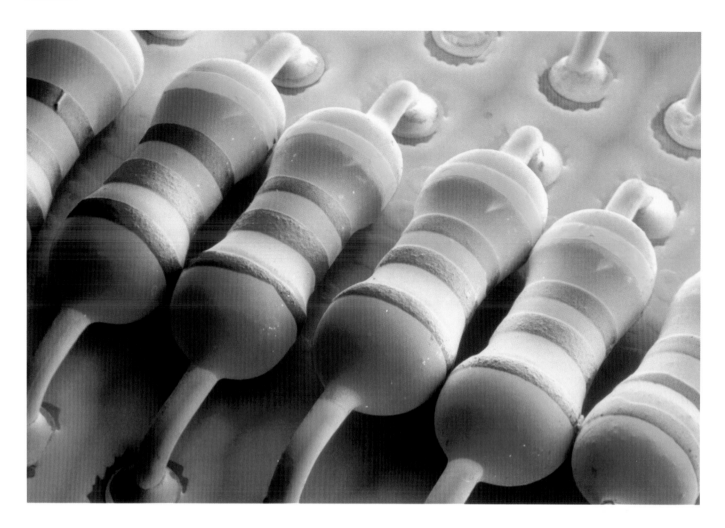

resistor, the atoms vibrate and generate heat. The power rating of the resistor is a measure of the rate at which this heat can be dissipated.

Making resistors

Many different types of resistors are needed in the electronics industry. Modern carbon resistors have many uses and are made in great numbers. They are made by mixing finely powdered carbon with an inert powder in the right proportion for the resistance required. The powder mixture is held together with a binder of liquid resin. The resistor is formed using a hot press to convert the powder into a solid rod. The rods are then molded into an insulating sleeve. Finally, each resistor is painted with a series of colored bands. The bands indicate the resistance value and accuracy of the device.

Highly accurate resistors can be made by putting a film of nickel and chromium onto a ceramic base. They can also be made by winding very fine resistance wires onto a ceramic tube and then covering the tube with enamel. Ceramic and wire-wound resistors generally have a higher power rating than carbon resistors.

Thick film resistors are made by screen printing a mixture of a resistive paste, glass, and cellulose onto a ceramic plate. These are then heated up to about 1830°F (1000°C), and a glaze is formed. These resistors are a type of integrated circuit and are often used instead of individual resistors.

See also: ELECTRONICS • ELECTRON TUBE • MICROELECTRONICS • PRINTED CIRCUIT • RESISTANCE • TRANSISTOR

Resonance

Making a child's swing go higher and higher by pushing it is an example of what physicists call resonance. A swing has a natural rhythm to its back-and-forth movement, and for resonance to take place, energy must be added in sync with this rhythm.

A back-and-forth movement such as that of a child's swing is called a vibration. The vibrations and the swing itself together make up a vibratory system.

If a vibratory system is set in motion and is then left uninterrupted, it vibrates according to its own natural rhythm until it slows down and eventually stops due to friction or air resistance. The natural rhythm varies from system to system, and it is measured by what is called its "natural frequency"—that is, the number of vibrations that take place in a fixed time (usually one second). The extent of each back-and-forth movement is called the amplitude.

To keep a vibratory system going at its natural frequency, energy must be added. The swing, for example, has to be pushed. Otherwise the amplitude will gradually decrease, and the vibrations will eventually stop. This slowing of the back-and-forth movement is known as damping. Damping is due to energy being lost from the system because of friction.

A force may be applied to a vibratory system in the direction of its motion and coinciding with the natural frequency of the system. This not only stops damping, it also increases the amplitude of the vibrations. It is for this reason that a swing goes higher and higher each time it is pushed, until it reaches its maximum height. Increasing the amplitude of a vibratory system to its maximum in this way is called resonance. Resonance transfers energy from the force applied to the vibratory system.

◄ *These photographs show the effects of mechanical resonance on the Tacoma Narrows Bridge, Washington. In 1940, a powerful gale caused the center span of the bridge to resonate and then twist. The resonance was so violent that it tore the bridge apart. The owner of the automobile trapped on the bridge managed to crawl to safety.*

DID YOU KNOW?

Soldiers marching in step will always break their step before crossing a bridge. They do this so that the rhythm of their marching does not make the bridge vibrate in such a way as to cause resonance, which might destroy it.

Mechanical resonance

Resonance in a mechanical system can be useful, as in the earlier example of pushing a child on a swing. Likewise, a diver on a diving board can gain the maximum height for his or her dive by jumping up and down in time with the natural frequency of the diving board.

Acoustic resonance

As a sound wave travels through the air, it makes the air vibrate. The more the air vibrates—that is, the greater the amplitude of the vibrations—the louder the sound produced will be.

Drawing a bow across a violin string does more than just disturb the air around the string. It also causes the top of the violin to vibrate at the same frequency as the string. More air is moved, creating a louder, richer sound.

In the same way, holding a vibrating tuning fork near an open tube will send sound waves down the tube, causing the air in the tube to vibrate. If the tube is of the right size and shape, the waves produced will be in the form called a standing wave. They will be reflected back and forth, from one end of the tube to the other, with a frequency that will cause resonance. As a result, the sound from the tuning fork will become much louder.

This effect is very important in the design of wind instruments, because the pitch of a note varies according to the length of the tube causing resonance. In the case of the pipe organ, different notes are produced by pipes of different lengths, each with its own resonant frequency. With brass instruments, the same effect is achieved by opening and closing valves that alter the length of the tube.

▲ *A violin uses resonance to amplify musical notes. Drawing a bow across the strings causes them to vibrate. The bridge of the violin carries the vibrations to the body of the violin, which resonates with the strings.*

Electrical resonance

A good example of how resonance is used in electrical circuits is in the tuning of a radio receiver. A radio receiver takes in energy from incoming radio waves. At any one time, however, the listener will only be interested in radio waves of the frequency of one particular station.

The receiver is tuned by making the resonant frequency of the circuit in the radio the same as that of the desired incoming signal. If the inductor (a coil of wire) and the capacitor (a component that stores electrical energy) are connected in the circuit so as to produce the greatest possible current, the signal received will be very loud. However, the inductor and capacitor may be connected in such a way that the voltage, and not the current, is at a maximum. In this case, the receiver's response to the resonant frequency will be reduced to a minimum.

These two types of circuits are known as acceptor and rejector circuits. When used together, a radio receiver can tune to a station on one frequency without interference from other stations on nearby frequencies.

See also: ELECTRIC CIRCUIT • MUSICAL INSTRUMENT • RADIO • SOUND

Respiratory system

The respiratory system is used to bring oxygen in the air into the body. People do this by breathing. Oxygen is used to break down food to release energy. The respiratory system also releases waste carbon dioxide gas produced by the body.

All animals have a respiratory system, which they use to take oxygen into their bodies and to release waste carbon dioxide (CO_2). This process is called gas exchange. All living things, except a few bacteria and other microorganisms, use oxygen to burn their food. This process, called respiration, releases the energy needed to stay alive.

Respiration

Food contains the nutrients needed for growing and maintaining the body. Food also supplies the energy used to power the body.

This energy is released as oxygen breathed in from the air reacts with the molecules that make up food. The energy is released in a controlled way by a series of chemical reactions that are collectively called respiration.

Respiration occurs in every cell of the body. Inside each cell, there are several smaller units, called mitochondria, in which respiration takes place. Cells that use a lot of energy, such as those that make up muscle tissue, contain many mitochondria.

The most common food used in respiration is sugar. The sugar reacts with oxygen to make carbon dioxide and water, releasing energy as a by-product

▶ *People cannot breathe underwater, so swimmers need to take regular breaths to take in enough oxygen to keep their muscles working. Athletes can continue exercising without enough oxygen—this is called anaerobic exercise. However, a consequence of anaerobic exercise is the buildup of lactic acid in the muscles, which causes cramp. This limits the amount of anaerobic exercise an athlete can perform.*

THE HUMAN RESPIRATORY SYSTEM

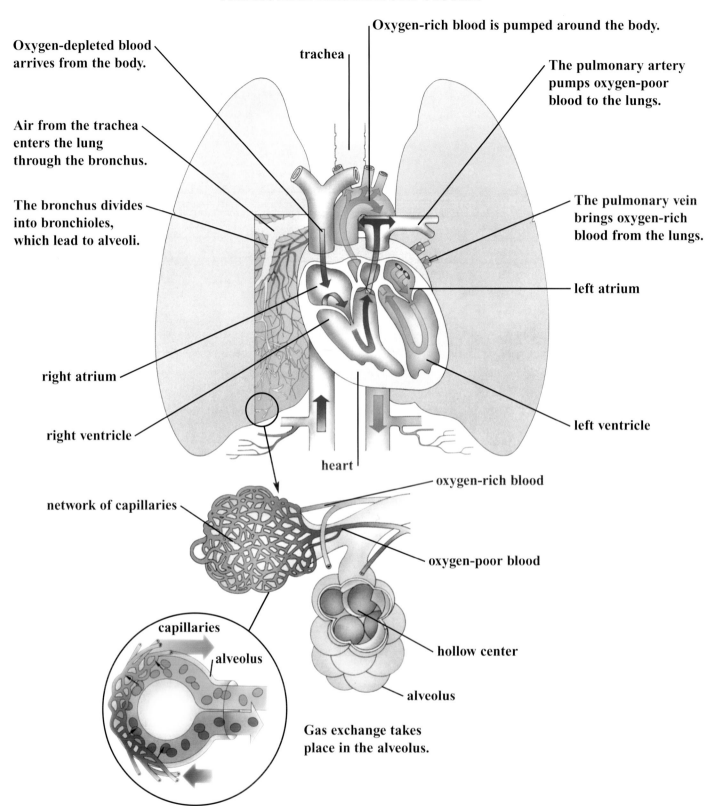

Oxygen-rich blood is pumped around the body.

trachea

Oxygen-depleted blood arrives from the body.

The pulmonary artery pumps oxygen-poor blood to the lungs.

Air from the trachea enters the lung through the bronchus.

The bronchus divides into bronchioles, which lead to alveoli.

The pulmonary vein brings oxygen-rich blood from the lungs.

left atrium

right atrium

right ventricle

left ventricle

heart

network of capillaries

oxygen-rich blood

oxygen-poor blood

hollow center

capillaries

alveolus

alveolus

Gas exchange takes place in the alveolus.

▲ *The lungs are connected to the heart by thick blood vessels, called the pulmonary artery and pulmonary vein. The heart pumps oxygen-depleted blood from the body, through the pulmonary artery, to the lungs. In the alveoli, the blood loses waste carbon dioxide and picks up more oxygen. This oxygen-rich blood passes back to the heart through the pulmonary vein. The oxygen-rich blood is then pumped by the heart around the body.*

of the reaction. The cell uses the energy to power important life processes. Cells consist mainly of water already, so any water produced during respiration just adds to the cell volume. Carbon dioxide is poisonous, so it has to be removed from the body by the respiratory system.

Gas-exchange surface

Oxygen (along with food molecules) is carried to cells by blood. The blood also removes waste carbon dioxide. The blood is pumped around the body by the heart. In addition to keeping the body supplied with everything it needs, the heart also transports blood to and from a membrane that is in contact with the air. This is called the gas-exchange surface, where oxygen is taken into the body and where carbon dioxide is released.

In small animals, such as worms, the gas-exchange surface might be the body itself. Many amphibians, such as frogs, use the insides of their mouths to exchange gases. Animals that live underwater exchange gases through feathery gills. Insects draws gases through hundreds of air tubes. Humans, however, and most other large animals that live on land breathe air into lungs.

How lungs work

The lungs are spongelike bags that are connected to the air by a thick tube called the trachea (windpipe). During breathing, fresh air is drawn into the lungs through the mouth and nostrils and down the trachea. Most animals, including humans, have two lungs, although some snakes have only one. The trachea splits into two pipes, called bronchi

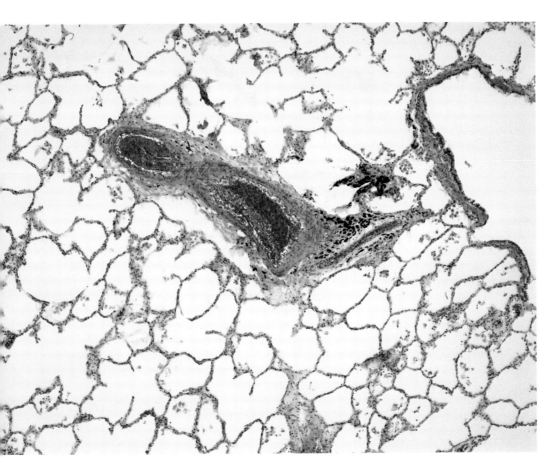

◄ *This microscopic image shows a slice through normal human lung tissue. An alveolus is clearly shown in the section in the center of the image. Alveoli are tiny air sacs in which gas exchange occurs. Inhaled oxygen diffuses into the bloodstream through tiny capillaries lining the alveoli. Waste carbon dioxide diffuses out of the blood to be exhaled.*

(*singular,* bronchus). Air passes into the lungs through each bronchus. The bronchi then continue to divide into a network of increasingly smaller tubes, called bronchioles. Each lung has thousands of dividing bronchioles. Each bronchiole ends in a lobe called an alveolus, which fills up with fresh air with each new breath. Together, the surface area of all the tubes and alveoli in a person's lungs is about 800 square feet (75 square meters)—nearly half the size of a tennis court.

Gas exchange takes place in the alveoli. Tiny blood vessels, called capillaries, bring blood cells to the surface of the alveoli. The gases pass through a membrane between the capillary and alveolus in a process called diffusion. This is a natural process that involves a gas moving from areas of high concentration to areas of low concentration.

Blood arriving at the lungs contains a lot of carbon dioxide but not very much oxygen. The air being breathed in is about 20 percent oxygen and has only a very small amount of carbon dioxide. Therefore, oxygen diffuses from the air into the blood, and the carbon dioxide diffuses into the air inside the lungs. The blood that leaves the lungs has therefore lost the carbon dioxide and picked up more oxygen. The air that is breathed out from the lungs is about 16 percent oxygen and also about 4 percent carbon dioxide.

▶ *These lungs were removed from a person who died from a smoking-related disease. Both the lungs are filled with thick, black tar. Tar and other chemicals in cigarette smoke cause lung cancer and many other dangerous diseases.*

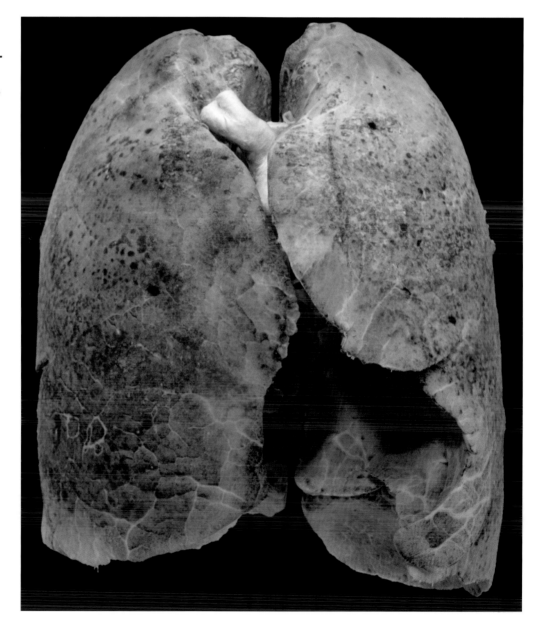

The blood carries oxygen in red blood cells. The cells are red because they contain a red pigment called hemoglobin. This chemical binds oxygen to the blood cell. Carbon dioxide can also bind to hemoglobin, but most of it dissolves in the plasma, which is the liquid part of the blood.

Breathing

People breathe without thinking. When relaxed, they take about 15 breaths a minute. When they are moving quickly, however, their bodies need more oxygen, so they breathe more quickly. Breathing is controlled by the brain stem, which detects how much carbon dioxide is in the blood. When there is a lot of carbon dioxide, the breathing rate increases.

Breathing makes use of air pressure to force air in and out of the lungs. The weight of the atmosphere pushing down on the surface of Earth creates a

▲ *Firefighters have to breathe the air inside breathing apparatus on their backs when they are fighting fires. This prevents them from breathing in dangerous fumes.*

DID YOU KNOW?

A breathing apparatus is used by divers to breathe underwater; by climbers at very high altitude, where the air is too thin to breathe; and by firefighters, when the air in burning buildings contains a lot of harmful smoke. The air is stored in a tank or bottle under high pressure. A valve on the tank controls how quickly the air comes out through a face mask. If it comes out too quickly, it can damage the lungs; too slowly, and the person will not get enough oxygen.

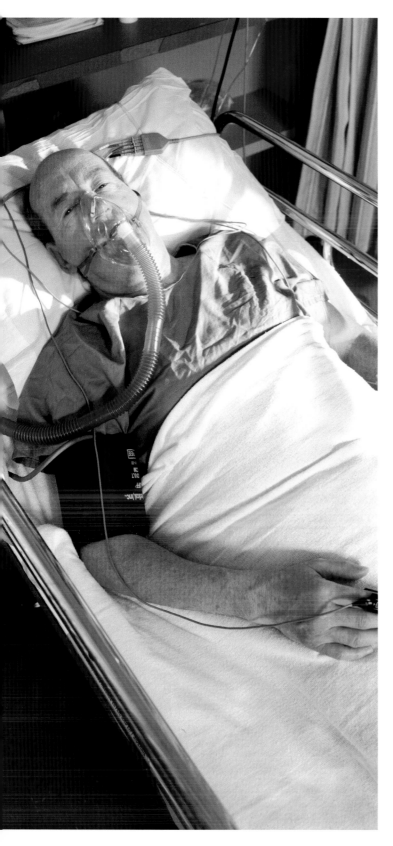

▲ *People sometimes need help to breathe. A machine called a respirator can breathe in and out for them, or an oxygen mask may be used to supply extra oxygen to help people breathe normally.*

pressure, known as atmospheric pressure. When a person breathes in, he or she is not physically sucking air in. Instead, atmospheric pressure is pushing air into their lungs.

To take a breath in, the volume of the lungs is increased by using the diaphragm. This curved sheet of muscle runs underneath the lungs. When the diaphragm contracts, it straightens out. This makes the ribcage rise and the chest swell, creating more space inside for the lungs. As a result, the pressure inside the lungs falls below atmospheric pressure, and air from outside rushes in.

To breathe out again, the diaphragm relaxes, and the chest returns to its original size. This pushes on the lungs and forces the air out of them.

Respiratory illness

The lungs are an essential part of the body. When they stop working properly, a person becomes very ill and is likely to die.

The most serious lung disorders are those caused by breathing in smoke and other tiny particles. People who smoke cigarettes, pipes, and cigars are especially vulnerable to lung diseases.

One of the most deadly diseases caused by cigarette smoke is lung cancer. Part of the lung begins to grow uncontrollably, forming a tumor. The tumor can grow so large that it blocks the tubes that carry air into the lungs, stopping the lungs from doing their job. As a result, the victim becomes breathless because he or she has fewer alveoli to supply the body with oxygen. Many lung cancers can be removed by surgery, but most sufferers never recover.

Emphysema is another lung disease caused by smoking. This disease causes the alveoli and other lung tissues to break down so gas exchange cannot take place. Sufferers are breathless and often have to have their arms and legs amputated because not enough oxygen is supplied to them.

See also: BRAIN • CELL • CIRCULATORY SYSTEM • DIGESTIVE SYSTEM • HEART AND BLOOD • NERVOUS SYSTEM

River and lake

Rivers and lakes are important sources of freshwater. Running water also helps to shape the land. Over many years, rivers carve out valleys and carry soil and rocks out to sea. Lakes can be small ponds or large inland seas, and a few have saltwater in them.

Some rivers start life as a melting glacier, while others are outlets of lakes. Many rivers flow from springs, where water comes out at the surface after seeping through tiny holes in rocks. Still more form as a result of rainwater runoff down hillsides and slopes. Slopes that catch and channel rainwater are called catchment areas. The amounts of water near the sources of rivers are small at first, but increase as rivers make their way toward the sea.

Most rivers can be said to progress through three separate stages: youth, maturity, and old age. The two main differences between these stages are the amount of water in the river and the gradient (steepness) of the land over which the river flows.

Youthful rivers

The youthful stage of a river starts at its source and includes the steepest parts of its course. For much of the year, youthful rivers may contain only a trickle of water. During heavy rains, however, or in spring when snow and ice melt, the stream may swell with water. At such times, even tiny streams can become raging torrents.

Fast-flowing streams containing plenty of water erode (wear away) the land. The beds of streams in the youthful stage are usually littered with loose rocks and boulders. Many of these have tumbled downhill into the riverbed from nearby mountain slopes. Fast-flowing streams can push this loose material downstream. Scientists have discovered that a stream flowing at ⅓ mile (0.5 kilometer) per hour carries fine sand along, while a river flowing at 6 miles (10 kilometers) per hour will push small stones downstream. A river flowing at 20 miles (32 kilometers) per hour can move boulders.

Running water itself does not erode the land very much. When running water sweeps sand, stones, and boulders downstream, however, these pieces of rock rub against each other and against the stones of the riverbed itself. In this way, they are gradually ground down into smaller and smaller particles. This process is called attrition.

The moving stones and boulders also loosen and erode rocks from the riverbed. For example, pebbles on the riverbed are swirled around by circular currents (similar to little whirlpools) called

▼ *The mighty Colorado River is the primary river of the southwestern United States. It gets its name because its headwaters are in the Rocky Mountains in Colorado, but the river finally drains into the Gulf of California.*

▶ *This picture shows a river in its youthful stage. It is cutting steeply through a mountain range, fed by groundwater running down from the surrounding slopes. Eventually, the river will erode its way down to sea level.*

eddies, cutting out deep potholes. These are common sights in the beds of streams in mountainous areas. This process is called corrasion. Rivers also react chemically with some rocks, slowly dissolving them. This process is called corrosion.

The total load of rock and soil carried by rivers is made up of about 70 percent solid material and 30 percent dissolved material. In these various ways, the youthful river cuts downward into Earth, giving the land through which it runs the steep-sided V-shape of a valley. Youthful rivers are often interrupted by rapids and waterfalls along their course. These are features that often occur when a river flows over hard rocks. Eventually, however, rivers erode even the hardest rocks.

Mature rivers

In its mature stage, a river flows down a gentler slope but carries much more water than in the youthful stage. The extra water comes from increased rain catchment and many more streams that join the main river. The water in the mature stage is usually darker than the clear water of the youthful stage, because attrition has crushed pieces of rock and sand into very fine particles called silt, which is carried in the moving water.

Youthful rivers tend to erode downward, cutting out deep and usually straight valleys. Mature rivers develop meanders (bends), and they tend to make their valleys broader rather than deeper. They do this by lateral (sideways) erosion. As the river sweeps around a bend, most of its force is directed against the outside of the bend. The land is undercut so that the meander is pushed outward and also downstream. On the inside of the bend, the current is much less strong, so much of the sand and silt carried by the river is dropped there. The slope on the inside of the bend is therefore gentle; the steepest bank and the deepest part of the river, where the current is most powerful, is on the outside of the bend.

Old age

Before a river empties into the sea, it passes through its final, old age stage. At this point, it is usually carrying more water than in either its youthful or mature stages, but the gradient is much less. In fact, rivers in old age flow slowly across nearly flat land. They usually follow a winding path and, when they are swollen by heavy rain or by melted snow and ice, they may overflow their banks. The flat land on either side of the river, called the floodplain, is then covered with water.

The water in the old age stage of a river is dark and muddy because it is carrying a large amount of silt. When the river floods, this fine silt is spread over the floodplain. The silt increases the quality of the soil, making it better for growing crops. The largest and heaviest particles are dropped first, on the river banks themselves. There they pile up in mounds called levees. Engineers often build levees up higher to prevent flooding, but this may cause the sediment to pile up on the riverbed. The effect is to raise the water level, so that the levees must be built up even higher. If this process continues long enough, the riverbed may eventually become higher than the land surrounding it.

Old age rivers often change course (direction). This may occur when rivers cut through the necks of meanders. Former meanders, no longer receiving new water, become oxbow (U-shaped) lakes. These lakes eventually dry up and become marshy meadows. Sometimes oxbow lakes are created artificially. For example, the Mississippi River Commission has cut through the necks of many large meanders along the lower Mississippi River. Straightening the river in this way has made the movement of people and goods by river faster.

River deltas

Although some rivers drain away inland, most end when they reach the sea. Some rivers enter the sea through long estuaries (inlets) where salty tidewater and freshwater mix. There, tidal currents help to sweep the river's load of rock and earth particles out to sea by flushing out the bed of the estuary. The particles, called sediment, are then spread over the seabed, building up in layers to form sedimentary rocks.

If the currents in the sea are weak, however, the particles carried by the river may be dumped at its mouth. There, where the river meets the sea, the sediment forms a new area of swampy land called a delta. When a river enters a delta, it usually splits

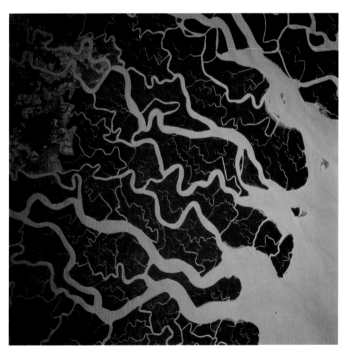

into several smaller streams. For example, the Mississippi River divides into several smaller streams, along whose course the sediment is dropped. This creates a so-called "bird's-foot" delta. On the other hand, the waters of the Nile River in Egypt spread out in the shape of a fan. This creates a delta shaped like the Greek letter *delta* (Δ).

Deltas are made up of fine sediment, which is often rich in minerals. As a result, they are often extremely good farmland. Deltas such as those of the Ganges and Brahmaputra rivers (in India and Bangladesh, respectively) are among the world's most densely populated areas. However, delta regions are continually threatened by destructive flooding.

Rivers and erosion

Rivers are the most important causes of erosion in moist, temperate regions. It has been estimated that every year about 8,800 million tons (7,980 million tonnes) of eroded rock are taken from all parts of the world and dropped into the sea. This is an average annual loss of about 200 tons per square mile (70 tonnes per square kilometer) of land. The rate of erosion varies greatly, however. In river basins, the rate of erosion is greatest on the steepest slopes and least on the floodplains near the sea.

U.S. scientist William Morris Davis (1850–1934) developed a theory called the cycle of erosion. Davis said that landscapes, like rivers, pass through the three stages of youth, maturity, and old age. In youth, moving bodies of ice, running water, and weathering erode newly formed mountain ranges. Eventually, the highest and steepest mountains are worn down to produce mature landscapes of rolling hills. In old age, when erosion is practically complete, all that is left is a peneplain (an almost flat plain).

At any time, however, a landscape can be interrupted by the uplifting of Earth's crust and returned to the youthful stage—thus forming a cycle. Davis called this return "rejuvenation." Other factors that Davis did not account for can also

◀ *The Ganges fan delta in Bangladesh is formed by the Ganges and Brahmaputra rivers. Annual flooding of the delta leaves rich alluvial deposits used for growing jute, the country's main cash crop.*

▲ *Lake Powell, created behind the Glen Canyon dam, is filled by the Colorado River. Over thousands of years, the Colorado River has eroded though the Colorado Plateau to form spectacular canyons.*

interrupt the erosion cycle and cause rejuvenation. For example, climate change can bring about increased rainfall, swelling rivers and giving them more erosive power. Similarly, falls and rises in the sea level, which occur during ice ages, can change the gradients of rivers.

Rejuvenation is the cause of the world's largest canyon, the Grand Canyon in Arizona. The Colorado Plateau was once a flat plain, nearly at sea level. This plain was slowly pushed up by Earth movements. This increased the speed of the Colorado River, which cut downward into the land.

Steep-sided canyons, such as the Grand Canyon, occur mostly in dry regions. In most other areas, valleys are constantly being broadened, and their sides are made less steep by the process of weathering.

Rejuvenation also creates features less dramatic than the Grand Canyon. For example, some river valleys contain a series of flat terraces on various levels. These river terraces are what remain of old floodplains. Each time the river was rejuvenated, it cut downward and wore out a new floodplain at a lower level. If, at the time of rejuvenation, the river was meandering, the deepening channel would have eaten into the underlying rocks. Its winding path is the shape of the original meanders, which are called incised meanders.

LAKES

Lakes are bodies of water enclosed by land. They range in size from small ponds to inland seas. Large lakes are similar to seas in many ways; for example, winds blow across them and produce waves that mold the shorelines in the same way as sea waves do. Deltas form where rivers flow into large lakes, and lakes even have small tidal movements called seiches. Although most lakes contain freshwater, some of the larger ones, such as the Great Salt Lake in Utah and the Dead Sea between Israel and Jordan, contain saltier water than the oceans.

Many lakes fill in hollows formed by Earth movements. For example, Lake Victoria in East Africa and Lough Neagh in Northern Ireland fill depressions in Earth's crust. Others, such as the Dead Sea and Lake Tanganyika in East Africa, are in rift valleys, formed when blocks of land sank between huge cracks in the crust. Volcanic craters are often filled with water. Sometimes lava from a volcano blocks a river valley, creating a dam behind which a lake forms.

Other lakes are formed by erosion of various kinds. Many were formed by the action of glaciers. In glaciated mountains, lakes called tarns occupy many cirques (armchair-shaped basins where small glaciers once formed). Many other lakes occupy the long, narrow hollows scraped out by glaciers. The Finger Lakes of New York State are examples. In lowland areas, lakes often fill basins or depressions made by the ice and then blocked by glacial moraine (rock debris carried by the ice). There are many such lakes in parts of Canada, Finland, and northwestern Scotland. The Great Lakes were formed as the glaciers of the last ice age retreated, between 14,000 and 4,000 years ago.

Lakes sometimes fill up hollows where limestone has been dissolved by rainwater. They are lined with clay, which stops the water from seeping away. In desert regions, wind-blown sand scrapes out some areas to a depth below that of the water table. (The water table is the highest level reached by water seeping through underground rocks in the area.) Such desert hollows become shallow lakes or swamps. Many oases are formed this way.

Oxbow lakes are created in river valleys when meanders are cut off. Along coasts, sea waves build up ridges of coarse gravel that eventually enclose saltwater lakes called lagoons. Other lakes are created artificially by dams so that the water can be used for irrigation or generating hydroelectric power.

Most lakes last only a short time in geological terms. Many exist only because the water table is higher than the floor of the lake. When the water table falls, the lakes disappear. Lakes may also drain away if a natural or artificial dam is broken, or if drainage from the lake becomes greater. Lakes also disappear by a slow process called sedimentation, which occurs when rivers dump their loads of sediment on lake beds. This sediment, and the plants that grow in it, eventually fill in the lake.

Changes in climate can also cause lakes to disappear. Some lakes in very dry regions are filled only after exceptionally heavy rains. Such lakes are called playas, and they are common in the southwestern United States.

FLOODING

About 12 percent of people in the United States live on land that is flooded from time to time. Housing and industry continue to be built up in these areas, so the damage and loss of life will increase unless people take steps to control the floods.

However, some floods can be useful. Delta areas are especially fertile because they are frequently flooded. Farmers in ancient Egypt depended on the annual flooding of the Nile River to cover their fields and leave behind fertile soil. The great Aswan High Dam, completed in 1970, was built to provide water for irrigation and hydroelectric power. However, the dam has stopped the annual flooding that fertilized the fields. Artificial fertilizers must now be used in the Nile valley, and this has created many other problems.

Protection against flooding can be divided into two distinct methods. One method tries to control the initial accumulation of dangerous levels of water; the other tries to control floodwaters and contain flooding within certain areas.

Controlling water levels

Water levels can be kept below the flooding point by reducing the rate at which water runs off from high land. This is done by planting trees, halting soil erosion, and improving methods of agriculture. All these efforts delay the runoff of water to the river and increase the amount of moisture stored in the soil. By plowing along the horizontal contours of the high land, instead of up and down, farmers trap water in the furrows, which gives the water more time to sink into the soil.

▶ *Crater Lake in Oregon is at the heart of Crater Lake National Park. Crater Lake is a volcanic lake, created by the eruption and collapse of Mount Mazama almost 7,000 years ago.*

◄ *The Thames Flood Barrier across the Thames River estuary in London, England, was constructed to protect the city against tidal flooding. Without the barrier, much of London would be underwater during a tidal surge.*

Managing flood waters

Floodwaters can be contained by building a dam across the river to form a reservoir. Built into the dam is a place for overflow, called a spillway, which controls the amount of water that is released from the reservoir to the river downstream. During a flood, water is released from the reservoir through the spillway at a rate that prevents serious flooding. This release rate is less than the rate at which water enters the reservoir. The difference between the two rates means that the reservoir fills up more slowly.

Most reservoirs now have other uses in addition to flood control. They are used for irrigation, hydroelectric power, and water supply. Chains of such reservoirs are to be found on some of the world's important rivers.

Often there is no suitable site for a large storage reservoir in the middle and lower parts of a river, so other types of flood prevention must be used. One example is the deepening of the river's channel by dredging. This process allows more water to flow through in flood conditions but, unfortunately, it may lead to problems with sediment deposits. Another method is to dig an additional channel alongside a river through cities and towns to take the overflow in times of flood. These additional channels are designed so that water flows into them only during a flood. Such channels either rejoin the main river farther downstream or are joined to other rivers.

It is also possible to build levees—high banks running alongside the river channel. They can be built of dirt or concrete. When floods occur, the levees can often stop the water from spreading over the surrounding land.

In times of unusually heavy rainfall or snow, the force of the water can become so great that it can burst through the levees, often with disastrous results. This happened in 1927 along the Missouri and Mississippi rivers. The levees were broken in hundreds of places, and land was flooded for 20,000 square miles (32,000 square kilometers).

Tidal flooding

Tidal flooding from the sea results in much the same problems as river flooding. However, the causes are quite different. Low-pressure zones (depressions) in the air over the sea can cause the water level beneath them to rise significantly. They will also produce strong winds. These conditions may cause a great surge of water, producing extra high water levels along the coast. These surges can be particularly dangerous if they happen at the same time as a high tide.

A serious incident of this kind happened in 1953 when a depression in the North Sea, between England and Holland, caused a surge to move southward. As a result, the water level in the Thames River estuary rose 6 feet (2 meters) higher than expected. The surge also caused a very high water level on the Dutch coast. Disastrous flooding resulted in southeast England and in the Netherlands, and more than 2,100 people lost their lives.

Protection against such tidal flooding can be afforded either by building high sea defense walls, or, in the case of an estuary, a barrier that has movable gates that can be raised and lowered.

See also: DAM • EROSION • GLACIATION • LANDFORMS • WATER CYCLE • WATER SUPPLY

Road and road construction

The first successful road builders were the ancient Romans. They built long, straight roads to link cities across their empire and carry their armies across Europe. The highways built all over the world in the last 50 years are some of the most incredible engineering feats in human history. A lot of work goes into road construction, including planning and surveying the route, shifting great loads of soil, and laying down the road surface.

▲ *This photograph shows a system of interchanges between metropolitan freeways. Interchanges are lanes that connect traffic from one freeway to another without interrupting the flow of traffic.*

The story of road construction starts in ancient Rome. Roman roads were built with heavy foundations (beds) that were 3 feet (1 meter) thick. The foundations were built using a mixture of small stones and cement, and the surfaces were paved with large, well-cut stone slabs. Although the paving was expensive, the Romans needed a good road surface because the roads had to be suitable for long marches by soldiers on foot.

By the time of the fall of the Roman Empire in 496 CE, Roman engineers had built an excellent system of roads linking every major town. Many Roman roads still survive, but most fell into ruin. Part of the reason no one paid any attention to them was that most journeys were short and most people traveled on horseback, so the cost of maintaining the paved Roman roads was too expensive. Starting in the seventeenth century, however, wheeled carriages became popular for travel, and the journeys became longer. The poorly maintained Roman roads made traveling uncomfortable and dangerous. Carriages often overturned because of the rise in the center of the roads that let water run off, or they became stuck in the mud. In addition, the iron tires used on the wheels of the carriages to make them wear better churned the roads into a mess.

The return to road building

In Europe, France led the way in improving the roads. In 1716, the French government set up a bridge and highway corps and a school for road building. Many leading engineers of the day went to work for the new government department. By law, French roads had to be laid with trees every 30 feet (10 meters) on both sides. Today, many country roads still resemble the beautiful tree-lined avenues of eighteenth-century France.

In spite of these improvements, French roads were still poorly drained. The early road beds, which consisted of pebbles piled atop larger stones, were flat. When water seeped through the pebbles, it could not run off this flat bed.

French engineer Pierre-Marie-Jérôme Trésaguet (1716–1796) adapted an earlier system of road construction to solve the problem of drainage. He built the foundation with a rise in the center, similar to the rise in the surfaces of earlier roads. This method allowed adequate drainage of the road, and it also used fewer stones. Trésaguet also introduced a better material for the surface. By

1775, Trésaguet's methods were being used throughout France. Other European governments did not seem interested in taking charge of road building, so Trésaguet's techniques and materials were not adopted in other countries.

The British started a planned program of road construction about 30 years after the French. They paid for the program by building turnpikes (toll roads), which meant that people were charged for using the roads. Tolls had to be paid for driving cattle and sheep along the road as well as for riding a horse or driving a vehicle. Two Scots pioneered road building in Britain. One was Thomas Telford (1757–1834), an engineer. He used a method very much like that of Trésaguet. The main difference was that he changed the road bed back to being flat. However, he solved the problem of drainage by carefully grading the stones in size.

The other outstanding Scottish road builder was John Loudon McAdam (1756–1836), who developed a new, low-cost surface material that became known as macadam surfacing. The new road surfacing consisted of layers of small stones cemented together into a hard surface by means of stone dust and water. This was pounded into place by a machine. By 1847, the roads in Britain were among the best in the world. In fact, people began to complain that the roads were so good that they encouraged drivers to go too fast. Macadam roads were later made of a bituminous material laid over tar.

In the Americas, the Incas, who ruled Peru from the thirteenth to the sixteenth centuries, built a fine system of roads. In other parts of South America and in North America, Native Americans used waterways for travel instead of roads. They had many land trails, but these were rough dirt paths suitable only for travel by foot. When the European settlers arrived, they needed roads for their horses and wagons.

At first, the European settlers simply widened the the Native American footpaths to make enough room for their wagons. The United States started to build turnpikes following the American War of Independence (1775–1783). The first such road was in Virginia, and it was backed by the state

▲ *John Loudon McAdam, shown here in an undated portrait, developed the macadam system of road construction while working as a surveyor for the Turnpike Trust in Bristol, England. In 1827, McAdam was made surveyor-general of metropolitan roads in England. He died at Moffat, Scotland, nine years later.*

government under a law of 1785. After 1792, however, the federal government turned road construction over to private companies. Some of the famous U.S. turnpikes of the early nineteenth century were the New York to Boston Post Road, the New York to Albany Road, and the Albany to Buffalo Road.

The greatest change came at the beginning of the twentieth century, when U.S. automobile engineer Henry Ford (1863–1947) popularized the Model T Ford as an affordable means of transportation. In the 1930s, the first modern highway system, called the Autobahn, was built in Germany.

Today, high-speed multilane highways link the major cities of most of the world's developed nations. The United States is covered by a fine network of state and interstate highways, and the dream of a Pan-American highway—linking the Northern and Southern hemispheres—is becoming a reality. Towns are now planned around the traffic flow, although in cities such as Los Angeles, this can cause another problem—air pollution. Proper planning and design of roads is now vital.

Road design

A highway administration must plan for the future. How many cars will be using the road in 20 years? Will the highway itself lead to more towns and thus more traffic? The effect of the road upon the landscape, the natural history of the region through which it passes, and the lives of the people in the area must all be taken into account.

Before any construction can begin, the land must be surveyed and all possible routes considered. Soil and rock samples will be taken from trial pits and bore holes along the proposed routes. The use of computers has made the work of road construction much easier. For example, computers are now used to calculate the grade line (level of a proposed route throughout its length), and the results can be displayed graphically on a monitor.

How many bridges and embankments will have to be built? How many rivers crossed and swamps drained? Will the road be affected by heavy snow,

> ### DID YOU KNOW?
>
> The interstate highway system is a network of freeways comprising some 42,500 miles (68,400 kilometers) of routes across the United States. The last link in the system, Interstate 105, was opened in 1993.

torrential rain, or hot sun? The designer must think very carefully about all these questions, and many others, before construction work can start.

Preparing the site

The highway administration assigns each job to a main engineering contractor. This contractor will hire several special subcontractors. The highway department itself will also send its own engineers to the site to ensure that all goes according to plan.

The first task is to clear a path for the new road. If any buildings are in the way, they must be demolished. Trees must be felled, and stumps or rocks are bulldozed or blasted out of the way. Temporary roads and bridges may have to be built to carry the construction vehicles. The site must be fenced off, and the soil must be drained with trenches cut out by excavators.

▶ **This map shows the interstate highway system linking most of the major cities of the United States. The first stretch of interstate highway opened in Topeka, Kansas, in 1956. It took another 27 years for engineers to complete the project. Hawaii has interstates H1, H2, and H3, which connect important military facilities on the island of Oahu. Alaska has no interstate highways.**

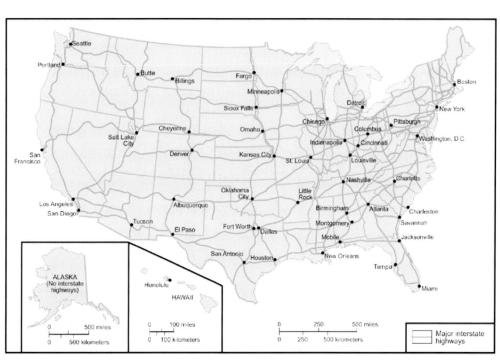

Earthworks

The construction machinery used during road building is enormous. Some machines are capable of shifting hundreds of tons of soil. Among the first to be brought in are the box scrapers. These machines are pulled by tractors on caterpillar tracks and pushed by bulldozers. Excavators and dump trucks are also brought in, and soon the route of the road takes shape as hills are leveled and hollows are filled. Embankments are built. Earth is firmly pressed down, smoothed, and leveled to provide a firm base for the highway.

While the earthworks are being prepared, bridges, underpasses, and supporting sections must be built, because traffic will need some way to cross the path of the highway during its construction. Supporting sections must be ready before the paving can begin.

When the earthworks are completed, more shallow trenches, about 4 feet (1.2 meters) deep, are dug for drainage. Pipes are laid in the trenches, which are then filled with gravel. Other pipes are laid to carry the water away.

Paving the road

Before the road is paved, the soil must be at exactly the right level. This is done by a scraper or grader, which is a wheeled machine with a steel blade mounted horizontally at the front of the machine.

The blade can be raised, lowered, or tilted by the scraper to cut a surface that is accurate to within about 2 inches (5 centimeters).

The first layer of paving, called the subbase, is then laid. This first layer consists of gravel or crushed rock, generally spread to a thickness of several inches. The subbase may be made firmer by mixing dry cement into the top layer, which is dampened and then dried to form a solid road base.

Methods of finishing the paving vary, but most of them use either blacktop materials or concrete.

Blacktop roads

Blacktop roads get their name from their black color. Bitumen (mixtures such as asphalt or tar) and stones are mixed together and heated. While the mixture is still hot, it is carried in trucks to the laying point and tipped into a large machine called a paver. The paver spreads out the mixture in a layer, which is then pushed down and compacted by a steamroller until the surface is firm.

This process is repeated until this layer, called the base course, is the required thickness. The top layer, called the wearing course, usually consists of asphalt. The surface of the road may then be roughened slightly to prevent skidding; bitumen-coated stone chip is rolled into the surface while it is still hot. A concrete base course can also be used for an asphalt wearing course.

Concrete roads

The final road surface is often in the form of concrete slabs up to 10 inches (25 centimeters) thick. To allow the concrete to expand or shrink, the slabs are jointed every 15 feet (4.5 meters) or so. Room for expansion is extremely important, because direct sunshine can heat the surface of the concrete slab to a temperature nearly 60°F (15°C) higher than that of the bottom of the slab.

Concrete slabs are often laid between temporary road forms—steel rails that support the edges of the concrete slabs while they are setting. The rails

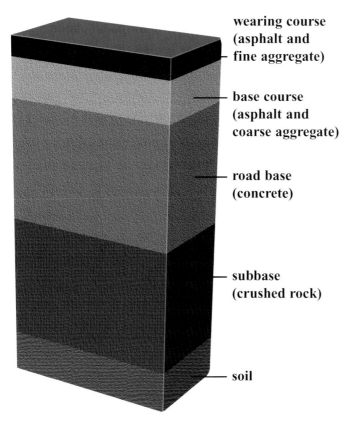

wearing course
(asphalt and
fine aggregate)

base course
(asphalt and
coarse aggregate)

road base
(concrete)

subbase
(crushed rock)

soil

▲ *This illustration shows the structure of a blacktop, or flexible pavement. The four layers of a blacktop are the wearing course, the base course, the road base, and the subbase. The overall thickness of the three layers is at least 15 inches (37.5 centimeters).*

are accurately laid to the required level. Along the empty road forms runs a concrete train, which is a mobile frame that includes a number of machines. The first is a placer spreader, which pours ready-mixed concrete between the forms. Other machines compact the concrete and trim it.

Similar to this method is "slipform" paving. Instead of using road forms, the side supports move along as part of a wheeled paver. The wet concrete is compacted with a much heavier vibration, which makes it set much quicker. This allows the side forms to travel along with the paver.

Concrete roads are often reinforced with steel mesh. The mesh holds the concrete tightly and allows for the strains and cracking caused by temperature changes and the accumulation of moisture. Reinforced concrete roads are more expensive to build, but they are stronger and generally last longer.

Similar to an asphalt surface, a concrete surface must be roughened to prevent skidding. The wet concrete can be brushed while still wet, but this may cause a high-pitched whine when cars drive over it at certain speeds. The problem is usually solved by adding a grooving machine to the concrete train. This machine makes irregular, noise-free grooves in the concrete.

Finishing the road

Once the paving is complete, road construction continues. The shoulders are filled with earth, and topsoil previously removed from the site is replaced. Shoulders and embankments are seeded with grass, and trees may be planted. Wildlife may return to live alongside rural highways. Indeed, to the surprise of conservationists, highway shoulders and dividing strips have sometimes proved to be popular with rodents and birds. Wildflowers that can survive exhaust fumes often spread in large numbers.

Safety barriers must be erected if there is no wide dividing strip in the center of the road. Safety barriers are also placed along raised sections of a highway and where embankments drop sharply. Lines marking lanes and junctions must be painted, and reflectors installed where necessary. Lighting is provided on roads in cities and towns and along some highways out of town.

Road signs warn of junctions, hazards, and lane movements, as well as providing drivers with information about directions and distances. Today, electronic signs are used on nearly all major routes. They show up-to-the-minute changes in speed limits in case of bad weather or an accident.

Emergency telephones are linked to a cable along most highways in case a motorist breaks down. Gas stations and rest areas are also added. Long-distance driving is tiring, and drivers must be encouraged to stop to rest if they are to drive safely.

Road maintenance

The amount of traffic on a modern road is very heavy. For example, the East Los Angeles Interchange, where four freeways meet, handles over 380 vehicles every minute. The United States

◄ *Three times as many road traffic accidents occur on highways at night as they do during the day. Street lighting helps reduce the risk of accidents, but the cost of installing street lights limits their use.*

has almost 4 million miles (6.5 million kilometers) of graded roads. Keeping them all repaired requires constant work.

ROAD SAFETY

About one-third of all injuries to people in cars are caused by the impact of their vehicle colliding with a roadside object, such as a lamppost. It is possible to design weak joints into the bases of lightweight lampposts, so that when hit by a car, the joint comes apart, allowing the car to continue moving without crashing to a stop.

One of the advantages of divided highways, where traffic moving in different directions is on different roads, is the reduction in serious head-on collisions. A barrier may not reduce the number of accidents, but it does make them less serious. If there is no barrier between the two roads, they should be at least 50 feet (15 meters) apart.

Crash barriers are essential. Gravel beds, into which vehicle wheels sink, have been tried, as well as rigid barriers. Plastic drums filled with sand, to slow vehicles down, have also been tested.

Road signs can lead to accidents if they are not absolutely clear. There is agreement between the United States and most countries in Europe that words on signs should be replaced with a common set of symbols that can be recognized worldwide.

In the United States, "rumble strips" have been built into road surfaces. As the car approaches junctions or unexpected curves, these strips produce noise and vibration to alert the driver.

Speed limits are one of the cheapest safety measures. When cars are moving at many different speeds, accidents are more frequent. Therefore, it is a good idea to keep traffic moving at a similar, suitable speed. Maximum speed limits do this by ordering cars not to travel faster than a certain speed. Minimum speed limits help traffic to move at a safer, average pace by speeding up the slower drivers. In the United States, varying speed limits are clearly posted.

See also: AUTOMOBILE • EARTHMOVER • LIGHTING • RUBBER • SURVEYING • TRAFFIC CONTROL

Robotics

Robots are often used in industry and even in a few homes. They are machines that can do the same job many times, without getting bored or tired as people do. Early robots did not look anything like people. However, the most advanced robots are now being designed to look and move like humans or animals.

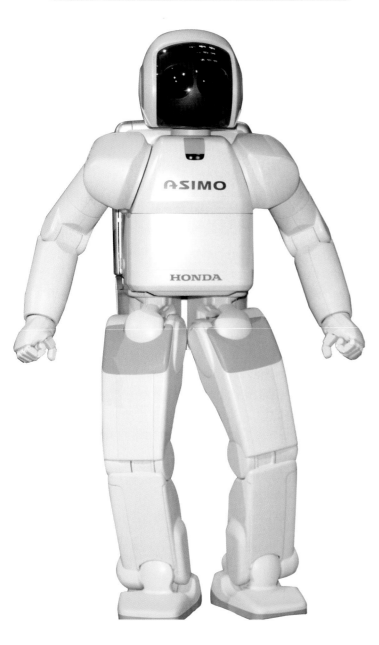

In science-fiction movies and books, robots are often made to resemble people. However, most simple robots in use today are machines with mechanical arms. These robots are designed to do a single job, such as pick up things, weld metals, tighten bolts, or sniff out gases.

Robots have been used to replace human workers in factories since the early 1960s. At first, they were simple machines designed to perform one task. However, they were designed to perform those tasks many times over without getting tired or making mistakes.

Over the last fifty years, robots have become much more complex. Many modern robots are designed to move around factories or warehouses on tracks or set paths and are used to carry heavy loads safely. As well as being used to perform simple tasks in factories and shops, robots are also used to reach places where people cannot go. For example, robots are used to check inside pipes that are too small for people to check easily.

Robots are also used in places that are not safe for people. For example, robots are used to check nuclear reactors or defuse unexploded bombs. Some advanced robots are even being used to explore other planets and moons in the solar system.

History of robotics

The idea of a robot has been around for hundreds of years. Simple machines, called automatons, were devices that moved on their own, generally powered by clockwork or a stream of water. In China, automatons were being made more than two thousand years ago, and they became popular in Europe sometime in the fifteenth century. Most automatons were moving dolls or working models of animals, such as birds. They were used mainly as toys and did not perform any useful work.

◄ *ASIMO stands for Advanced Step in Innovative Mobility. It is the world's most advanced humanlike robot. ASIMO was developed by Honda in 2000 and can move in the same way as a human being.*

◀ *Many factories are equipped with robots. The robots work on assembly lines, where they perform the same tasks over and over again. In this picture, the robots are welding auto parts at an automotive plant.*

perform a wider range of tasks than the early robots of the 1960s. Robots that resemble people and animals have a wider range of movements than robotic vehicles that move on wheels. While wheels need a road or track to roll along, legs can walk, run, and climb over objects.

The latest robots are also sensitive to touch and can see using cameras, even recognizing simple objects and patterns. Robots of the future will be so complex that they will probably be controlled by a type of computer called a neural network. Neural networks are computers that work like the human brain. They do not have to be programmed; instead, they learn how to work or can be taught by a human teacher. The most advanced robots will learn how to control their bodies and how to perform different tasks in the same way that a baby learns how to walk and talk.

DID YOU KNOW?

In the 1940s, Russian-born U.S. science fiction writer Isaac Asimov (1920–1992) introduced the idea of the "Three Laws of Robotics" to ensure that robots would always be under control and safe to use.

1. A robot may not injure a human being or allow a human being to come to harm.
2. A robot must obey orders given by human beings, except where such orders conflict with the first law.
3. A robot must protect itself, as long as such protection does not conflict with the first and second laws.

In 2004, a sci-fi movie entitled *I, Robot* (starring Will Smith) was made, based on Asimov's novel.

The word *robot* was first used by Czech author Karel Capek (1890–1938) in his play *R.U.R.: Rossum's Universal Robots* (1920). The play was about a country in which all work was done by mechanical workers. The word comes from the Czech, meaning "forced labor."

Ever since, people have thought of robots as being mechanical people that exist only in movies and books. Only very recently, however, have robots been designed to resemble people and animals. Modern robots are more intelligent and can

The industrial robot

Most robots are used in factories. The basic design has not changed very much since the first industrial robots were developed in the mid-twentieth century. Most have powerful mechanical arms that are jointed in several places, so they can move around in all directions.

A simple robot has three parts: a hydraulic power unit, a mechanical arm, and a computer control system. A robot's movements are produced by hydraulics, which involves a thin oil, called hydraulic fluid, being pumped from tanks into cylinders. The cylinders contain closely fitting pistons. The fluid pushes on the piston, forcing it out of the cylinder. The piston is attached to a moving part of the robot. As the piston moves, so does the moving part. Similar to the muscles in an arm, hydraulic pistons work in pairs. One piston will push on the arm so it bends. The other piston in the pair will push in the opposite direction so the arm straightens. Each piston also pushes its opposing pair back into the cylinder.

The mechanical arm is the part that picks things up, sprays paint, tightens nuts, or welds metal. Most arms are able to move in all directions. They can swing up and down, swing from side to side, and move back and forth. At the end of the arm is a "wrist," where a tool, such as a drill, is fixed. The wrist is jointed like the arm so that it can also move in three directions, and it can rotate around in either direction as well. The jointed arm and wrist give the robot a great degree of movement.

Robotic programming

The feature that makes a robot different from other machines is that a robot can be adapted to new situations. Many modern machines are controlled by simple computers called microprocessors. They are used in everything from an automated teller machine (ATM) to a laser printer. However, these devices, which have a combination of moving parts all controlled by the computer, can only work together to perform a single set of tasks. Laser printers can only print documents, for example. It cannot be made to edit text, while an ATM cannot be taught to sell train tickets.

By contrast, robotic arms can be fitted with the appropriate tool and then programmed for a particular job. Programming a simple industrial robot consists of an operator running it through the movements involved in the task it is to perform.

The human operator may move the robot arm by hand. With larger robots, the operator usually uses a control pad or joystick to move the robot. Some robots have a teach mode. In this mode, they can

▶ *Aibo is a robotic pet dog manufactured by Sony. The robot can be taught tricks and even likes being stroked. Aibo can fetch bones, play dead, and wag its tail in the same way as a real dog. It even knows when its battery is running down and can recharge itself.*

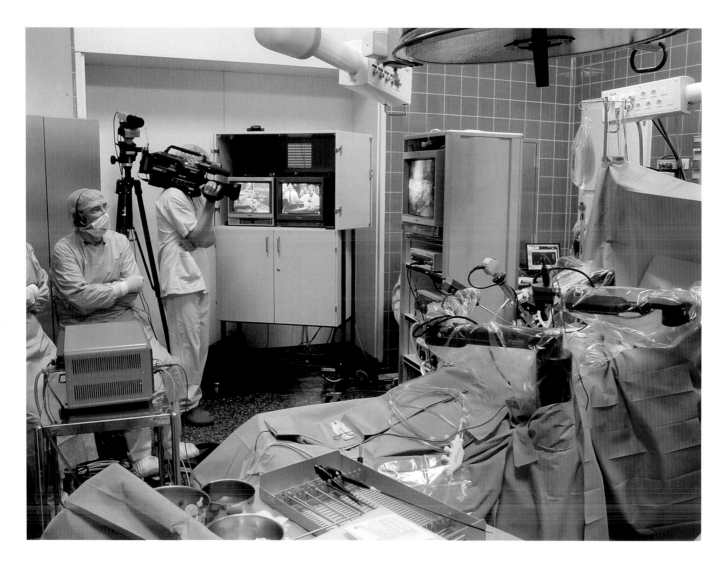

remember the exact sequence of movements that the operator performs. Other robot control systems are programmed with the final positions of all the movements the robot needs to make and the order in which they are to be made. The robot will then move between each of these preprogrammed positions. This second programming phase results in more precise movements.

Computers and engineering

Robotics draws on many different areas of science and engineering. As programmable machines, robots are controlled by computers. The control unit of a robot arm must coordinate the hydraulic systems, which is a relatively simple task. Artificial intelligence (AI) is an important part of modern robotics. AI is a type of computing that involves a robot learning how to perform new tasks.

▲ *Robots are being developed to perform complex surgical procedures. The robot may be controlled by a surgeon in another room or even in another country. This form of surgery is known as telesurgery.*

Some robots need to move around and get past obstacles easily. Robot engineers learn how to build more mobile robots by studying how the bodies of animals and people move around. The area of engineering and computing that is involved in this process is called cybernetics.

Sensors

A robot is required to work without a human operator. To do this, it must know where it is, where it needs to go, and what to do when it gets there. To achieve this, the robot's computer builds a model of its surroundings, so it can move safely without bumping into things.

People and animals build a similar model in their minds. Information from the senses, such as sight, touch, and hearing, keeps the model updated. Robots have senses as well. A robotic sense of touch is created using a system called a force feedback loop. This system allows a robot to know if it is trying to put a square peg in a round hole, for example. The robot hand measures the amount of force pushing on the peg, and this measurement is supplied to the computer brain. If the force is too large, it means the part does not fit, and the hand is withdrawn. The same system can be used to control the amount of force used by a robot hand to grip an object. Therefore, the same hand can be used to pick up a delicate object, such as an egg, as well as a heavy object, such as an iron bar.

Giving a robot a sense of sight is a more complex task. A picture of the surroundings can be produced using a video camera. However, the robot's computer control must be able to identify what is in the picture.

Images are full of information. A small black-and-white television image contains at least 8 million units of information; a standard television signal contains more than thirty of these images every second. A robot could therefore spend a lot of time processing images. However, most of the information in the image does not change and is not important for the robot's job. Instead, the robot is programmed to look out for certain patterns, such as the shape of the component it needs to pick up from a conveyor or a particular color on the object or place it needs to move toward.

Coordination

Robots are designed to shut down if something goes wrong. Robots are often working with heavy objects and moving them around quickly, so accidents could be dangerous. Therefore, robots have safety systems that predict when an accident might occur. The safety system must shut down the faulty system but keep other components working so objects are not damaged. The robots might also be required to coordinate their operations with other machinery, including other robots. The safety and coordination systems are controlled by expert systems—large databases of rules that tell the computer what to do in various situations.

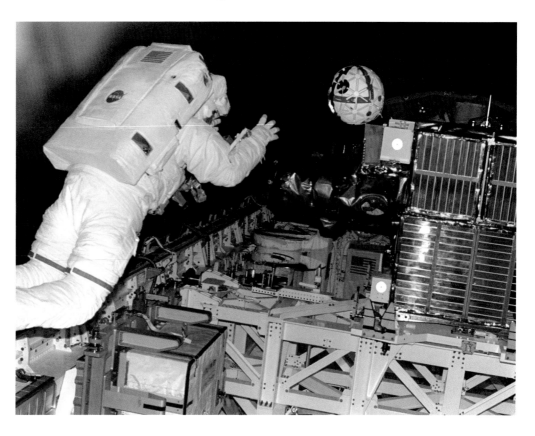

▶ **This astronaut is about to grab a spherical robot, which is a remote control camera used to take images of the shuttle while it is in orbit.**

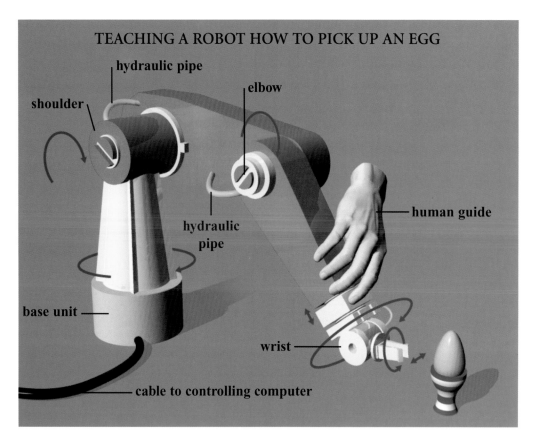

TEACHING A ROBOT HOW TO PICK UP AN EGG

hydraulic pipe

shoulder

elbow

hydraulic pipe

human guide

base unit

wrist

cable to controlling computer

◄ *Robots need to be programmed to perform exact movements. To do this, a human operator guides the robotic arm through a series of movements to pick up an object such as an egg. The robot's computer then stores the various movements in its memory so that the robot can perform the task by itself.*

Living with robots

When fifty robotic welders were installed at a DaimlerChrysler automobile plant, they replaced two hundred employees and produced 20 percent more automobiles. Robots work at a constant pace without spending time socializing, taking breaks, or making mistakes. They do not have to be protected from high temperatures and hazardous materials in the same way that people do. Occasionally, they do break down, but people often get sick and are unable to work. Industrial robots spend around 5 percent of the year being repaired, maintained, or reprogrammed. However, the average human worker is off work for one-quarter of his or her work time every year.

Robots have allowed DaimlerChrysler and other automobile manufacturers to make cars less expensively. However, what was good for automobile companies has not necessarily been good for society. Although the workers replaced by robots are free to perform other jobs, many of these jobs do not pay as well or require as much skill as the jobs now being performed by the robots.

Robots have also taken over the jobs that are too boring or difficult for people to do. For example, inspecting the quality of tiny electronic parts soon affects the eyes of a human worker. A person can only perform this job for a few hours at a time before getting headaches and eyestrain, but a robot does not get tired. Robots are also used to do repetitive jobs, such as packing boxes. Human workers soon get bored, and this leads to accidents. Doing the same movement over and over can also cause repetitive strain injuries in human workers.

Nanorobots

Robots are already used to perform complicated surgical procedures. Robots made using nanotechnology will be billionths of an inch long. One day, these robots might crawl around the human body or swim through the blood. In this way, nanorobots could be used to treat diseases or repair damaged organs.

See also: ARTIFICIAL INTELLIGENCE • SOFTWARE

Rock

Rocks are composed of grains of minerals. However, while minerals have a specific chemical composition, rocks do not. The amounts of minerals in any rock are not the same from one sample to another. Rocks are not always solid—soil and mud are also forms of rock.

Geologists classify rocks according to the processes by which they were formed. Three main types of rocks are recognized: igneous, sedimentary, and metamorphic.

Igneous rocks

Igneous rocks are created when hot liquid rock, called magma, cools and solidifies. Magma comes from Earth's interior, and it is a mixture of different elements that occur naturally in Earth's crust. When the magma cools, these elements combine to form minerals. For example, granite is a rock formed from magma that has cooled slowly underground. It is a crystalline rock, which means it consists of the crystallized grains of several minerals, including feldspar, mica, and quartz.

▼ *A stream of molten lava flows from an erupting volcano. Lava is magma that has erupted onto Earth's surface from deep underground.*

▲ *These impressive rock formations in Arizona are made from sandstone. After the sandstone has been exposed, it has been eroded into unusual shapes by swirling, abrasive winds. Sandstone is a sedimentary rock, comprised of compacted and cemented sediments.*

Granite is called an intrusive igneous rock because the magma has intruded into other rocks under pressure. Other intrusive igneous rocks include diorite, gabbro, pegmatite (which may contain huge crystals), and syenite.

Other igneous rocks consist of magma that has cooled on or near Earth's surface (lava). These are called extrusive igneous rocks. The best known extrusive igneous rock is basalt, which is hardened lava. Basalt covers 200,000 square miles (518,000 square kilometers) or more of the Columbia and Snake River region in the states of Washington and Oregon. This basalt was formed when lava poured out from huge fissures (cracks) in the ground. Basalt also forms much of Earth's oceanic crust.

Some magma reaches the surface during volcanic explosions, which shatter the magma into pieces ranging in size from volcanic dust and ash to large, loaf-sized lumps called volcanic bombs. The ash often buries the surrounding land. When dust and ash are compressed, they form a rock called tuff.

Other examples of extrusive igneous rocks include pumice, which forms from frothy magma containing bubbles of gas, and obsidian, which is a volcanic glass. Extrusive igneous rocks cool and harden quickly. As a result, there is no time for crystals to form, and the rocks are fine-grained or even glassy in appearance. It is only possible to identify the minerals in extrusive igneous rocks using a powerful microscope.

Sedimentary rocks

Many sedimentary rocks are formed from the worn fragments of other rocks. These are called clastic rocks. They include conglomerates, which are formed from pebbles set in silt or sand; tillite, which comprises material worn by glaciers; loess,

DID YOU KNOW?

It is not always necessary to travel to canyons, cliffs, and mountains to examine rocks. Even in big cities, rocks are all around. People cut rocks into blocks and slabs to use for building and paving. With a basic knowledge of what different rock types look like, it is possible to explore the buildings and sidewalks in a town or city and identify a surprising number of different rocks.

which consists of wind-blown silt or dust; sandstone, which is composed of grains of sand; siltstones, consisting of silt; and mudstones and shales, which are composed of fine mud and clay.

Most of these sedimentary rocks form in straight or nearly straight layers called strata on the beds of lakes or seas. However, some red sandstones are cross-bedded, that is, the strata are tilted and not in straight lines. Such rocks were formed from sand dunes that piled up in deserts millions of years ago.

Two things must occur before loose sediments can become hard rock. First, the sediments must be compacted by the weight of sediments lying on top. Second, the grains must be lithified (cemented together) by minerals left behind when water seeps between the grains. Lithifying minerals include iron oxides, which often turn rocks red; calcite; dolomite; and silica, another common mineral.

Limestones, including chalk, are also sedimentary rocks. Some limestones are composed of the remains of tiny sea animals and plants. Others are made up largely of shells and animal skeletons. Still other limestones are chemical in origin. For example, oolitic limestone consists of millions of rounded grains that resemble fish eggs. The grains include a core made of sand or a small piece of shell. Around this core are layers of the mineral calcite, left behind when the water evaporated. Other chemically formed sedimentary rocks include rock salt and rock gypsum, formed when seas dry up.

Coal is an organic sedimentary rock. It is made up of the compressed remains of ancient plants and animals. Many inorganic sedimentary rocks also contain traces of once-living creatures, called fossils. Sedimentary rocks cover about 75 percent of

▼ *The white cliffs near Dover, England, are formed from chalk. This crumbly rock is sedimentary. It forms when the shells of billions of tiny dead organisms settle in layers on the bottom of seas and harden over time. The shells are made from calcium carbonate ($CaCO_3$), which gives the rock its characteristic color. Geological processes may later lift layers of chalk above the surface.*

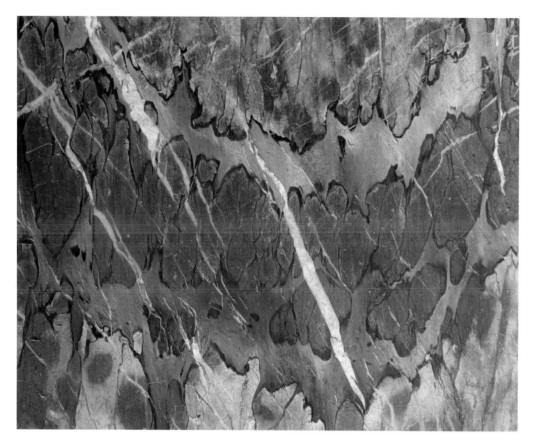

◄ *This photograph shows a cross section through a layer of marble. Marble is a metamorphic rock produced when limestone is subjected to great heat and pressure by geological processes. These processes recrystallize the minerals in existing rocks and mold them into different layers and bands.*

the world's land surface area. However, in the top 10 miles (16 kilometers) of Earth's crust, at least 95 percent of the rocks are either igneous or metamorphic in their origin.

Metamorphic rocks

Metamorphic rocks are rocks that have been greatly changed, usually by enormous heat and pressure. Metamorphism is similar to the process of baking, when soft dough is turned into something that looks quite different—bread. The heat and pressure are often supplied when huge masses of magma rise through the rocks in Earth's crust, or when Earth movements raise up high mountain ranges. When these events occur, the minerals in existing rocks may be recrystallized or rearranged in different layers and bands. Metamorphism also sometimes occurs when mineral-rich fluids come into contact with existing rocks.

Examples of metamorphic rocks include marble, which was formerly limestone; hard slate, which was once soft shale; and quartzite, which was formerly a sandstone containing a lot of quartz.

Rock cycle

Earth systems that produce rocks are continuous and are still happening today. The creation of some new rocks is spectacularly obvious. Extrusive igneous rocks, for example, are often formed by volcanic eruptions. However, most of the processes involved in producing new rocks are far too slow to observe and therefore go unnoticed.

All new rock is created from old rock in a process called the rock cycle. Even rocks from the highest mountain peaks are eventually recycled and may, possibly, become a completely new type of rock. The processes involved depend on temperature, pressure, time, and changes in environmental conditions in Earth's crust and at its surface.

The recycling of rocks works like this: Magma, moved by convection currents deep in Earth's molten interior, is forced into or through Earth's crust and solidifies either at or below the surface to form new igneous rocks. As the rocky plates that comprise Earth's crust (tectonic plates) move slowly against each other over time, uplifting occurs, forming mountains made of these igneous rocks.

The exposure of rocks to weathering at Earth's surface eventually breaks them down into small grains. These grains are then transported by gravity, water, and wind and are eventually deposited as sediments. This process of weathering and deposition is called erosion. The eroded sediments are deposited in layers and become compacted and lithified to form sedimentary rocks.

Variation in temperature, pressure, or the chemistry of rock may cause chemical or physical changes. With igneous and sedimentary rocks, these physical changes cause the formation of metamorphic rocks. When exposed to higher temperatures, for example, by subduction back under Earth's crust, metamorphic rocks (or any other rock type) may be partially melted, resulting in the creation once again of igneous rocks. The cycle then starts over again.

Rock structures and landscape

The study of rocks is called petrology. However, petrology is not limited to how rocks were formed and what they are made of. Rocks also have a great effect on landscape. For example, hard rocks such as granite and marble resist erosion much longer than soft shales and siltstones. Hard rock strata often protect softer rocks beneath them. Many of the impressive rock pillars, buttes, and mesas of the American West are capped by hard rocks. Eventually, however, even these formations will be worn away, because weathering and erosion will undercut the softer rocks.

▼ *This diagram shows how the rock cycle works. The rock cycle is the process in which molten material from Earth's mantle is injected into the crust, where it passes through various rock stages before returning to the mantle or becoming fixed in the continental crust.*

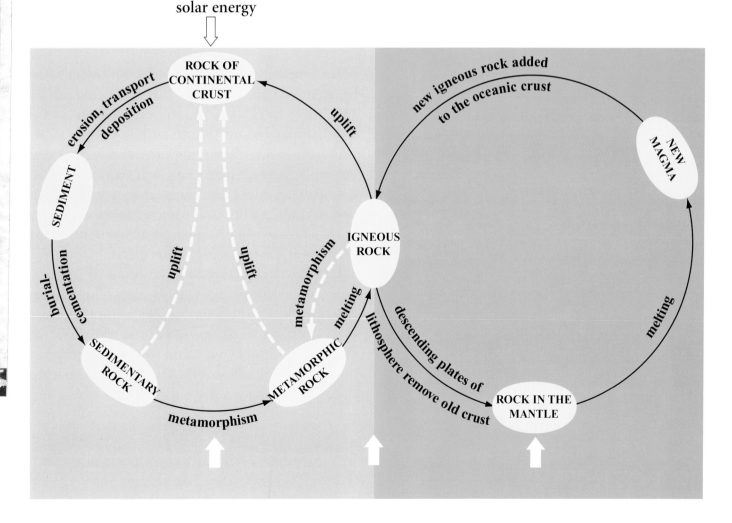

CRUSTAL CIRCUIT
solar energy

MANTLE CIRCUIT

▲ *These mountains of the Sierras on the West Coast of the United States are composed of granite. Granite is an igneous rock, formed from magma that has cooled slowly in or above Earth's crust. Many mountain ranges are made from granite that has been uplifted by geological activity to great heights.*

Limestone is a rock that produces a distinctive type of scenery. Limestone contains the mineral calcite (a form of calcium carbonate; $CaCO_3$). Calcite reacts chemically with water and carbon dioxide (CO_2) and dissolves. As a result, rain and river water wear holes and channels through limestone surfaces. As water flows through these holes and channels and drains into the rocks below, it erodes huge caverns and chimneys. When caves collapse, gorges are formed.

Igneous rocks also form distinctive landscapes. Devil's Tower, Wyoming, is the remains of a mass of molten rock that cooled underground.

Tectonic movements also affect rocks and scenery. Lateral (sideways) pressure squeezes flat strata into upfolds called anticlines and downfolds called synclines. Tilted and folded rocks can often be seen in exposed cliffs. When the top of an anticline is worn away by erosion, hard strata tend to remain as cuestas (ranges of hills), while softer strata are worn down to form low-lying vales. When the tectonic plates on Earth's surface collide, sedimentary rocks on the seabed are squeezed upward into gigantic and complex folds. The rocks of the Himalayas in Asia have been compressed by as much as 400 miles (645 kilometers).

Many rock structures are the result of up-and-down or sideways movements along huge faults (cracks) in Earth's crust. Block mountains are blocks of land lifted up between faults, while rift valleys are blocks of land that have slipped downward. The edges of the faults often form steep slopes called fault scarps.

> **See also:** ELEMENT, CHEMICAL • EROSION • GEOLOGY • MINERAL • MOUNTAIN • PLATE TECTONICS • WEATHERING

Rocket

Rockets were first used as weapons, about one thousand years ago. Rockets are still used as weapons, carrying explosive warheads, but their most important use is in space exploration. Without rockets, the Apollo astronauts would not have reached the Moon.

In a simple rocket, burning fuel produces large amounts of gas. This gas is forced out of an exhaust nozzle at the back of the rocket, causing the rocket to move forward. The principle of rocket propulsion is explained by the third law of motion, proposed by English scientist Isaac Newton (1642–1727). This law states that for every action there is an equal and opposite reaction. The forward force of a rocket (the reaction), is equal to and in the opposite direction of the backward exhaust force, called thrust (the action), generated by the engine. The greater the thrust, the greater the reaction and the greater the rocket's speed. Since the exhaust gases do not push against anything at the rear, a rocket can operate even better in space than in the atmosphere, where the exhaust gases are slowed down by the air.

The force of a reaction can be experienced, for example, when a boat is pushed off a bank to move it out into the water. As a person pushes against the bank, the bank exerts an equal but opposite force on the person. This force is transmitted through the person's body to the boat to make it move.

If the boat is in the middle of a lake, it can be made to move by pushing on another boat. Assuming that the boats are both stationary, the push will make them move in opposite directions. A rocket works in exactly the same way, except that the rocket engine produces the gas that pushes against the rocket. Unlike a jet engine, the rocket needs no air supply. It carries everything it needs to make the gas. Rockets can therefore work in outer space.

History of rocketry

Rockets appeared soon after the invention of gunpowder around the tenth century CE. In a gun, gas produced by the burning powder causes an

◄ *This picture shows the space shuttle* **Atlantis** *during its launch from Cape Kennedy, Florida, in July 2001. Space shuttles use two solid-fuel booster rockets and a main liquid-fuel rocket engine for launch into space.*

▲ *A hybrid rocket motor is tested at NASA's Stennis Space Center. Hybrid rockets combine elements from both solid- and liquid-fueled rockets. In this rocket, liquid oxygen is used to burn solid fuel.*

explosion, which propels a ball or bullet from the gun. In a rocket, the gas is allowed to escape in one direction, and the rocket moves in the other direction.

Rockets used by the Chinese in the thirteenth century were simply arrows with a tube of gunpowder tied to them. The end of the tube near the point of the arrow was blocked. The other end of the tube was left open, so that the powder could be lit and the gases could escape. These crude rockets resembled modern fireworks.

Rockets soon spread to Europe. They were used, for example, by the French under Joan of Arc (1412–1431) during the defense of Orleans in 1429. However, with the improvement in guns and artillery, rockets went out of use in warfare until the late 1700s, when they were used against the British in India. English inventor William Congreve

(1772–1828) then developed the rocket into an effective weapon. He made it more accurate and equipped it with an explosive warhead.

By the 1850s, accuracy was further improved by English inventor William Hale (1797–1870), who installed curved vanes in the rocket nozzle. This caused the rocket to spin, and the spinning made it travel much straighter. This effect is called spin-stabilization.

By the late 1800s, people had begun to realize that the rocket could be used for space travel. Russian space scientist Konstantin Eduardovich Tsiolkovsky (1857–1935) studied rockets seriously, and his work led him to be the so-called "father of space flight." However, it was in the United States and Germany that the most important pioneering work was carried out. In the United States, the so-called "father of modern rocketry" Robert H. Goddard (1882–1945) launched the first liquid-fueled rocket in 1926. In Germany, a team under Wernher von Braun (1912–1977) developed the notorious V-2 rocket, which was used to bomb London during the Blitz of World War II (1939–1945). The V-2 bomb is the direct ancestor of all modern rocket missiles and space rockets.

Solid propellants

The substances that propel a rocket are called the propellants. Two types of propellants are needed in a rocket. One is the fuel, and the other is the oxidizer, which is the substance that provides the oxygen needed to burn the fuel.

The gunpowder used to propel firework rockets is a solid propellant. It has charcoal (carbon) and sulfur as fuel and saltpeter (potassium nitrate; KNO_3) as an oxidizer. Different kinds of solid propellants are used in space rockets. They are particularly used to give added thrust for takeoffs. The space shuttle uses strap-on solid rockets for

takeoff, as does the Delta rocket, one of the oldest and most reliable of the U.S. space-launch vehicles. Solid propellants contain a type of synthetic rubber as fuel and substances such as ammonium chlorate (NH_4ClO_3) as oxidizer.

Solid-propellant rockets are of very simple design. They are little more than a cylinder packed with propellants, with a nozzle at the end to let the burning gases escape. The cylinder also acts as the combustion chamber, where the fuel is burned.

Liquid propellants

The rockets used for space launches use liquid propellants. Liquid propellants produce much greater thrust than solid propellants. The main rocket motors of the space shuttle burn liquid hydrogen (H_2) as fuel and lox (liquid oxygen; O_2) as the oxidizer. When these propellants combine, they produce water (H_2O) and give out great heat. The water forms a gas, which expands and escapes at high speed through the rocket nozzle. Other rockets use kerosene or hydrazine as fuel.

Liquid-propellant rocket motors are much more complicated than solid-propellant rockets. The propellants are carried in separate tanks and are pumped into the combustion chamber by separate turbopumps. There they are ignited. Liquid-propellant rockets have the great advantage that their speed can be lowered and they can be stopped and started easily. On the other hand, solid-propellant rockets are very difficult to control once they start burning.

A liquid-propellant rocket is very powerful, but by itself it cannot launch a spacecraft into orbit. For a space launch, several rockets must be linked together, one atop the other. The bottom rocket fires first, boosting the rockets above it to a higher speed. When its fuel has run out, the bottom rocket drops away. The second rocket then fires and boosts the rocket above it to still higher speeds. Eventually the top rocket, carrying the spacecraft, is traveling

◄ *This photograph from World War II shows a German V-2 rocket being fueled. These rocket-powered missiles were launched against London during the war. The V-2 provided the basis for all modern rocket engine designs.*

SOLID-PROPELLANT ROCKET ENGINE

▶ *In a solid-propellant rocket, the propellant burns from the inside out, and the combustion products are forced out of the nozzle, causing an opposing thrust.*

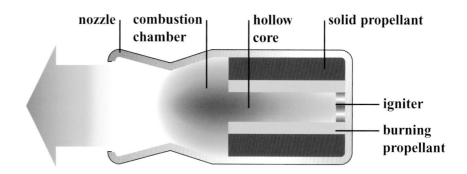

nozzle | combustion chamber | hollow core | solid propellant | igniter | burning propellant

LIQUID-PROPELLANT ROCKET ENGINE

▶ *Liquid-propellant rockets also generate thrust by expelling combustion gases. The amount of thrust can be controlled by adjusting the flow of fuel and propellant into the combustion chamber.*

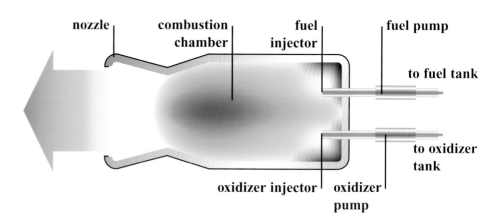

nozzle | combustion chamber | fuel injector | fuel pump | to fuel tank | to oxidizer tank | oxidizer injector | oxidizer pump

fast enough—at 17,500 miles (28,000 kilometers) per hour—to go into orbit. This system of rockets is called a multistage (many step) rocket. All space launch vehicles use stages.

The Delta rocket has two main liquid rocket stages, one atop the other. Nine solid rocket boosters are strapped onto the first stage. In a similar way, the space shuttle can be described as having two stages. The solid boosters make up the first stage, and the main liquid-fueled engine makes up the second.

Future rockets

Powerful rockets such as the liquid hydrogen/liquid oxygen type have a major drawback. To achieve their high thrust, they must burn several tons of propellants every second. So even with a huge rocket such as *Saturn V,* the fuel soon runs out. This limits how far space vehicles can travel.

While trips to the Moon are possible, trips to other planets would be impossible with the present generation of chemical rockets. So scientists have come up with many ideas for more suitable rockets. Some of these ideas may sound like science fiction. They include the photon rocket, which would be propelled by powerful beams of light, such as lasers. Another is the nuclear pulse fusion engine, which would use controlled hydrogen-bomb explosions.

However, more practical rockets have also been designed that could soon improve the prospects for long-distance space travel. They include the ion and nuclear rockets. Both of these types have already been successfully tested by the National Aeronautics and Space Administration (NASA).

See also: FORCES • MISSILE AND TORPEDO • MOTION • SPACE SHUTTLE

Roller coaster

Roller coasters carry people around a kind of elevated railroad at amusement parks. The cars are propelled up a steep slope and then roll at high speed around the rest of the track. The ride is exciting because there are lots of ups and downs and twists and turns; sometimes the cars even go upside down.

Roller coasters are so called because once the cars, which roll on wheels, are propelled over the top of the first slope (called the lift hill), they coast around the rest of the track without further power. As the cars go up the lift hill, they gain a large amount of potential energy. As the cars go over the top of the hill, this potential energy is converted to kinetic energy, as gravitational force accelerates the cars down the slope on the other side. As the cars continue by inertia around the rest of the track and up and down its hills and loops, their energy constantly changes between potential and kinetic. However, the overall energy of the cars continually falls, so designers must ensure that the initial, potential energy stored at the top of the lift hill is enough energy to carry the cars through all of the features to the end of the ride.

Roller coaster history

Most old-fashioned roller coasters were huge constructions of metal, timber, and concrete. They were very awkward to build, needed a lot of maintenance and were not very safe. Gradually, they went

◁ *This picture of the* **The Pepsi-Max Big One** *on Blackpool Pleasure Beach, England, shows the cars moving down the first steep drop of the ride. When* **The Pepsi-Max Big One** *opened in 1994, this drop was the highest on any roller coaster in the world. The first drop needs to be steep to provide the speed and inertia to carry the cars around the rest of the ride.*

▲ *Cars on the* **Roar** *roller coaster bank around a turn in Six Flags Marine Park, California.* **Roar** *is one of a number of new wooden roller coasters that have benefited from modern technological improvements.*

out of fashion and often they were dismantled, although sometimes this was difficult. In fact, the huge *Cyclone* roller coaster at Coney Island, New York, was so complicated that it was considered impossible to dismantle.

Steel roller coasters

Modern roller coasters are faster and safer than the old wooden roller coasters, and they can be dismantled and changed around more easily.

Instead of wood and girders, most modern roller coasters are made from sections of strong tubular steel or box-section steel beams with tubular tracks. These can be shaped into many different curves, twists, and loops, and are so strong that they are nearly self-supporting. These advantages of steel mean that steel roller coasters can have many more complex features than were previously possible using wooden construction methods.

The complex forms that modern roller coasters take are created using three-dimensional computer models. In this way, designers can experiment cheaply and easily with many imaginative designs on screen, while the computers calculate the speeds and forces that will be generated by the different designs. A designer's objective is to reach a final design that fits the requirements of the amusement park, is structurally sound, and is safe for passengers.

Once the design has been completed, the manufacturer prefabricates the steel track and supports in large sections before transporting them to the site for final assembly and testing.

Roller-coaster cars are usually made of strong steel frames with tough, molded, fiberglass bodies. Various exterior trim and fittings are added to make the cars look more exciting. Passenger safety restraints are always built into the cars, which will not start moving until the restraints have been locked into place. On some rides, simple lap bars are used; for more extreme rides, shoulder harnesses and other restraints keep passengers firmly in place.

Roller-coaster cars use a system of opposing wheels to run along and secure themselves to the track. On steel roller coasters, the wheels are usually made from polyurethane or nylon. On wooden coasters, the wheels are usually metal.

Most cars use a system of two upper wheels, one side wheel, and one lower wheel at each corner. The upper wheels run along the top of the tubular track and take most of the weight of the cars. The other wheels grip the track from the side and underneath to reduce vibration and ensure that the car stays on the twisting ride. With rides that include upside-down sections, there are two lower wheels. When the cars are upside down, these become the upper wheels and take the weight of the cars hanging below. Wheels are coated with Teflon, which is very slippery and allows the cars to travel faster.

Increasingly, the cars on many roller coasters have become more unusual, as designers seek to provide ever-greater thrills. Some cars run above the track in the usual way, but the cars are floorless, so that passengers' legs swing around underneath them as they are flung around the ride. In other cars, passengers are secured standing up.

Many cars, however, run below the track. By running underneath the track, the height of a roller coaster is emphasized, as passengers can see straight down to the ground. Suspended cars swing under the track from a pivoted joint, adding an additional side-to-side motion to the ride. Inverted cars are rigidly attached to the track, which gives designers more control over the movement of the cars.

▶ *This roller coaster at the Seattle Center Fun Forest, Washington, is a basic steel coaster, with small cars running on top of a tubular-steel track.*

New wooden roller coasters

Although most roller coasters of recent years have been of the steel type, there has been a renewed interest in wooden coasters, and a number of new rides have been built around the world.

Wooden coasters offer a different kind of ride from steel coasters. There are no popular modern features such as loops or corkscrews that turn riders upside down on wooden roller coasters. Neither are there floorless, stand-up, or hanging cars. However, modern roller-coaster technology, unavailable at the time of the original wooden coasters, means that these traditional-type coasters can still be great fun and provide an equally thrilling ride.

Wooden coasters have a wooden framework that supports a thin metal track. The route that the track takes is less complicated than that on most steel coasters, but it includes steep hills, long drops, twists, and banked turns. Because the track is often more simple to construct, wooden roller coasters are often longer than their steel counterparts.

Because the cars on wooden coasters do not loop-the-loop or corkscrew, the cars are simpler, and riders do not need to be so tightly restrained. Riders move slightly in their seats and can rise a little during the drops, adding to the exhilaration of the ride.

Propulsion systems

Traditionally, roller-coaster cars are dragged slowly up the lift hill by a chain-drive system. The wait for the top helps build anticipation for what is to follow, but it means that the ride does not start immediately. It also reduces the running efficiency of the ride for the operators.

In recent years, as roller-coaster designers have created bigger thrills by increasing track contortions and creating radical new cars, propulsion systems have also received attention. Instead of being towed up a lift hill by a chain, cars on some rides are blasted up it by giant catapult or by more complicated compressed-air or hydraulic systems. One of the fastest launches is made by *Hypersonic XLC* at Kings Dominion, Virginia. Using a compressed-air system, it accelerates from 0 to 80 miles (0 to 130 kilometers) per hour in just 1.8 seconds.

The latest propulsion systems use linear electric and linear synchronous motors (LEMs and LSMs). These types of motors work using opposing lines of powerful, switching electromagnets. Linear motors can be as long as required, so cars can be propelled all the way up a lift hill. Using LEMs, *Superman The Escape* at Magic Mountain, Los Angeles, is able to propel its large, 6-ton (5-tonne) cars up to 41 stories high at 100 miles (160 kilometers) per hour.

▲ *The cars of this inverted roller coaster run below the track so that the passengers are suspended with their legs dangling.*

See also: GRAVITY • MOTION

Rubber

Rubber is a stretchy substance with many uses, the most important of which is the manufacture of tires for wheeled vehicles. The amazing properties of natural rubber have prompted scientists to study its chemical structure very closely. This study has resulted in the production of a range of synthetic alternatives to the natural material.

▲ *In a process called tapping, spiral grooves are cut into the bark of a rubber tree. The rubber tree leaks a milky latex, which runs down the grooves and into a container. The latex dries to form crude rubber.*

Natural rubber is obtained from the rubber tree, which is native to South America. The rubber is in the form of a milky, white juice called latex, which oozes from the bark. The Native Americans of Central and South America called the rubber tree the *cahuchu,* which means "weeping wood." They used latex for making simple waterproof shoes and sheets. The English word *rubber* comes from the fact that an early use of latex in Europe was for erasing pencil marks.

By the late eighteenth century, people had discovered that latex dissolved in turpentine could be used to make cloth waterproof. Raincoats made this way were called macintoshes, named for their inventor, Scottish chemist Charles Macintosh (1766–1843). Elastic bands, hoses, tubes, and shoes were other early items made of rubber.

Uses of rubber

By 1840, chemists had learned to make rubber stronger by heating it with sulfur in a process called vulcanization. While being vulcanized, the rubber could be molded into many different shapes.

With the invention of the bicycle, automobile, and other wheeled vehicles, the manufacture of tires became the largest single use for rubber, and this remains so even now. Early tires were made of solid rubber. Since the 1890s, pneumatic (air-filled) tires have been used for larger road vehicles.

As well as tires, an automobile may have up to six hundred different rubber parts. Rubber is used to make drive belts, rollers, and seals for many machines. Rubber can be stretched up to four or five times its length and still return to its original shape. This elasticity makes rubber very useful.

Rubber is still used to waterproof clothes such as aprons, raincoats, and boots. Other articles, such as elastic tapes, have rubber added to make them more stretchy. Waterproof rubber also prevents air from escaping from air mattresses, inflatable boats, and life rafts. Electric cables are covered with rubber because it does not conduct electricity.

Rubber plantations

In 1876, the British Government sent English botanist Henry Wickham (1846–1928) to Brazil to collect seeds from the rubber tree. The seeds were sprouted in a greenhouse at Kew Gardens near London and then taken to Sri Lanka and Malaysia. These plants were the start of the huge plantations of rubber trees, which now produce most of the world's natural rubber.

▲ *Natural rubber is a polymer that consists of many thousands of isoprene (C_5H_8) units.*

▲ *Gutta-percha has the same chemical formula as natural rubber, but the arrangement of the atoms within the molecule is slightly different. Gutta-percha is said to be an isomer of natural rubber.*

natural rubber

vulcanized rubber

▲ *In a process called vulcanization, natural rubber is heated with sulfur. Sulfur atoms form cross-links between the rubber molecules. Vulcanized rubber is stronger than natural rubber and more elastic over a greater range of temperatures.*

The hevea rubber tree grows best in warm, moist climates in well-drained soil. On plantations, the tree grows to about 60 feet (18 meters) tall. It has dark leaves, pale yellow blossoms, and smooth bark. The latex flows through a network of tubes that lie just under the bark.

The latex is collected by cutting a groove into the bark of the tree trunk. The groove slants downward toward a cup that is attached to the tree near its base. Latex oozes from the cut, flows down the groove, and drips into the cup. Workers called tappers make fresh cuts and collect the latex. About one cupful of latex is collected from each cut. Later, a new groove is carefully made. Over the years, the bark grows back over the old cuts.

After collection, the latex is filtered to remove leaves and twigs. It is then placed in tanks of water. Adding a chemical, such as an organic acid, causes the latex to coagulate (clump together). The clumps of latex are then pressed together between rollers to produce sheets of raw latex.

After the latex has been rolled into sheets, it is hung on racks in a hot room for several days. Some latex is concentrated by being whirled around at

▼ *A worker hangs latex sheets on a drying rack at a rubber plant in Thailand.*

▶ *A block of polyurethane rubber foam is rolled through a factory in Mexico. This rubber is used to protect electronics, computers, and household appliances.*

high speed inside a centrifuge. This form of latex is often used to make sponge rubber. After the remaining water has dried out of the rubber, it is pressed into bales and sent off to factories. Some liquid latex is left, and it is shipped inside tanks.

Making rubber products

At the factory that processes rubber, the dry rubber from the plantations is first treated to make it softer and more plastic (able to be molded). The rubber is then chopped into small pieces and mixed in much the same way as a baker mixes bread dough.

The next stage is to mix other compounds with the rubber. Sulfur is the main ingredient, which hardens the rubber in a process called vulcanization. Colored substances, called pigments, add color to the rubber. Fillers such as clay make the rubber easier to handle but do not improve its strength.

A rubber product is made into its final shape by a number of methods. For example, rubber may be rolled into sheets. Extrusion is a process in which soft rubber is pushed through a hole to make long strips of rubber. Items such as shoes and tires are made by pressing the soft rubber into a mold.

Synthetic rubber

The word *synthetic* describes rubber that is made in a factory rather than the rubber obtained from a tree. Synthetic rubber is made from coal and oil.

The first synthetic rubber was produced during World War I (1914–1918), when Germany could not get supplies of natural rubber. Early artificial rubber was of poor quality, but it improved as chemists learned more about how to produce it.

By the time of World War II (1939–1945), good synthetic rubber could be made from coal and oil, and large amounts were used. Chemists discovered that synthetic rubber was better than natural rubber for some purposes. For example, automobile tires include synthetic rubber to help them grip the road when it rains.

The world now makes more synthetic rubber than natural rubber because synthetic rubber is less expensive and has a greater number of uses. However, the price of synthetic rubber depends on the price of oil.

SBR rubber

SBR, short for styrene-butadiene rubber, is the most common form of synthetic rubber. Styrene is made from coal, and butadiene comes from crude oil. These two chemicals react to form long chains, called polymers, in a process called polymerization. The styrene-butadiene polymer forms a synthetic latex, which can be used to make objects or can be mixed with other types of rubbers.

Neoprene and nitrile rubbers

These rubbers are very good at resisting attacks by oil, sunlight, and oxygen. They are used for oil seals, diving suits, and gasoline hoses.

Polyurethane rubbers

Polyurethane rubbers are strong and stand up well to heat and wear. Polyurethane rubber foams contain many tiny air pockets that make them useful for heat insulation and fire-resistant furniture.

▲ *Tire production uses up most of the world's rubber supply. Rubber is easy to mold and can grip the road in wet weather. It is also strong and flexible enough to carry the weight of heavy vehicles.*

Tire manufacture

The largest single use for both natural and synthetic rubbers is for tires. Rubber tires grip the road well and also give a smooth ride. The first pneumatic tires were made fifty years before the automobile was invented. They were invented by Scottish engineer Robert William Thomson (1822–1873) in 1845 and ran for 1,000 miles (1,600 kilometers) on his horse-drawn carriage.

Modern tires are made of three materials: rubber of various kinds, steel wire, and fabrics. The different parts of the tire are made separately. The parts are then brought together and formed into the familiar tire shape. Finally, the tire is vulcanized by heating it in a mold.

How tires are made

Different kinds of rubber are needed to make different parts of the tire because each part has to do a particular job. For example, the tread must be tough enough to resist wear on the road. For this reason, it is made of a rubber with some fine carbon powder mixed in it. The side walls must be able to withstand continuous stretching around the wheel. At the same time, they are being bent and extended every time the wheel turns and the weight of the car pushes down a different part of the tire.

The bead, which is the part inside the tire that grips the wheel, consists of a number of wires embedded in tough rubber. This rubber has more sulfur in it than the other rubber components.

The inside of the tire consists of layers of nylon coated with rubber. This is called the casing. The nylon thread is woven into a fabric with many threads running along its length but very few across it. This gives the fabric great strength in one direction but allows it to bend without too many knots at the points where the threads cross. The fabric is covered on each side with a thin layer of rubber and then cut into strips, called plies, to make up the casing.

Special tires

Race cars use tires made of a special rubber. A tire gets very hot at high speed, and heat affects the way the rubber behaves. Rubber used for the tread of race car tires works best at high temperatures. Warming the tires up before the race begins is very important. This is one of the reasons that there is a warm-up lap before Indycar or Grand Prix races.

Tractors and earthmoving equipment used for freeway construction also need special tires. They must be able to withstand enormous loads and give the machine a good grip in the worst possible conditions. The tires of earthmovers are enormous, which helps spread the vehicle's weight over a large surface area and keep it from sinking too far into the ground. Aircraft also must have tires specially made to handle the weight and power of aircraft during takeoff and landing.

Winter weather presents particular problems for tire manufacturers. Tires intended for driving in snow must have very deep treads. Snow tires may also have metal spikes called studs. In some states of the United States, however, studded tires have been banned because they damage road surfaces.

See also: POLYMERIZATION • SULFUR

Rutherford, Ernest

New Zealand–born British physicist Ernest Rutherford was one of the great pioneers of atomic physics. His studies of radioactivity and the nucleus led to modern scientific theories on the nature of the atom.

Ernest Rutherford was born in Nelson on the South Island of New Zealand on August 30, 1871. Rutherford's family had emigrated from Scotland to Nelson in 1842. His father, James, raised flax and ran a sawmill. His mother, Martha, was a schoolteacher.

From an early age, Rutherford showed good all-around ability as a student. In 1887, he went to study at Nelson Collegiate College. Two years later, he was awarded a university scholarship to study at Canterbury College, Christchurch. After receiving a bachelor's degree in 1892, Rutherford embarked on advanced research in mathematics and physical sciences. His research on the magnetic properties of iron using high-frequency electrical discharges won him a first-class master's degree in 1893. The work also enabled Rutherford to construct a highly sensitive detector for radio waves.

In 1894, Rutherford was awarded the Exhibition Science Scholarship, enabling him to study at the Cavendish Laboratory at Cambridge University in England. There, he worked as a research student under English physicist J. J. Thomson (1856–1940). Armed with his radio detector, Rutherford made the first successful wireless transmission over 2 miles (3.2 kilometers).

Transformation of elements

At around that same time, two discoveries were made in continental Europe that determined the course of Rutherford's research at Cambridge. In 1895, German physicist Wilhelm Röntgen (1845–1923) discovered X-rays, and in 1896 French

▲ This undated portrait shows Ernest Rutherford wearing his academic gown. Rutherford received many awards and honors during his lifetime, including the 1908 Nobel Prize for chemistry.

physicist Antoine-Henri Becquerel (1852–1908) discovered radioactivity. Thomson suggested that Rutherford join him in studying these two new phenomena. In 1898, Rutherford discovered alpha and beta particles in uranium radiation, and he also identified some of the properties of these particles.

In 1898, Rutherford became professor of physics at McGill University in Montreal, Canada. There, Rutherford worked with the radioactive element thorium. He observed that it gave off a gaseous

◄ *A researcher from the Oak Ridge Y-12 plant in Tennessee holds a disk of weapons-grade uranium. In his experiments with uranium, Rutherford observed two different kinds of radioactive emanations, which he called alpha radiation and beta radiation.*

radioactive substance. Rutherford enlisted the help of English chemist Frederick Soddy (1877–1956) to isolate and identify this unknown substance. Soddy demonstrated that the gaseous substance was an element called radon. Rutherford and Soddy announced their theory of radioactivity in 1902. Their work overthrew the scientific law stating that matter could neither be created nor destroyed. In recognition of the importance of this work, Rutherford was awarded the Nobel Prize for chemistry in 1908.

Return to England

In 1907, Rutherford accepted a post as professor of physics at Manchester University. His time there was to prove his most productive. In 1910, Rutherford established the revolutionary idea that the atom is not solid but consists of a dense nucleus surrounded by orbiting electrons, similar to a miniature solar system.

During World War I (1914–1918), Rutherford worked for the British Royal Navy. His research on submarine detection consumed his work at Manchester for the next four years. In 1919, he resumed his work and made yet another contribution to the science that was to become nuclear physics. He succeeded in disintegrating a nitrogen atom by bombarding it with alpha rays.

In 1919, Rutherford was appointed Cavendish Professor at Cambridge University and returned to reorganize the Cavendish Laboratory there and to promote the study of nuclear physics. In 1920, Rutherford predicted the existence of the neutron, which was discovered by English physicist James Chadwick (1891–1974) in 1932.

A respected teacher and leader, Rutherford was much admired by his students. He was good humored, with a loud, hearty voice, and was always full of encouragement and enthusiasm. Many honors were bestowed upon him, including the Order of Merit (1925) and a knighthood (1914), and he was made a baron in 1931. He wrote more than 150 scientific papers and several books before he died in 1937 at the age of 66.

See also: ATOM AND MOLECULE • CHEMISTRY • PHYSICS • RADIOACTIVITY

Safe and vault

A safe is a strong box where money, jewelry, and important papers are kept to protect them from being stolen by thieves or destroyed by fire. Safes are usually made of iron or steel and have locks that are very hard to break open without a key or combination. A vault also protects valuable items, such as cash and jewels, but it is much larger, often as big as a very large room.

Just about every business has a safe of some kind. Many homes have them, too, when people wish to keep large sums of money or expensive jewelry with them rather than in a bank.

Banks store cash and other valuables in very secure rooms called vaults. They have very thick doors and high security. Most vaults are kept underground so there is only one way in and out.

Business safes are generally much larger than those fitted in private homes, but they work in much the same way. There are two types of safes—money safes and record safes. Money safes guard jewelry, cash, and documents. Record safes hold business and personal records and are designed to protect the contents in case of fire or flooding.

Since they are meant for protection, especially against theft, money safes are usually made of solid steel or iron and are built to be as burglarproof as possible. They are built so that tools, explosives, or metal-cutting equipment cannot break through and open them easily. Basic money safes are metal boxes with a strong lock. Others are enclosed in a block of steel and reinforced concrete, which makes it harder for thieves to move them or force them open.

To preserve important papers against fire, record safes are made of thin steel rather than the heavy steel used to make money safes. The metal is insulated so that it does not melt easily. Record safes are usually mounted on wheels and have

▶ *This small safe could be used to store valuables in a home or an office. These safes are small enough to be hidden from view, for example, in the floor. This makes it even harder for thieves to get at the valuable items inside.*

▲ *This safe is fitted with a combination lock. To gain access to the safe, the wheel has to be turned in a very exact way. The wheel is turned until the arrow lines up with a certain number. Then it is turned in the other direction until another number is aligned. This may continue for several turns until the correct combination of numbers has been completed.*

Locks

Money safes and vaults have locks that are different from those on the doors and windows of a house. The lock on a money safe or vault is only one of several devices used to stop potential thieves. The lock itself does not have to be as strong as that on the front door of a house. The lock on a money safe is protected by the hard steel of the safe's door. If

▼ *Banks store money and other valuables in huge underground vaults. Bank vaults have thick doors and several locks. Bank vaults are also very heavily guarded, so it is difficult to get in without permission.*

rectangular doors. Their design makes them fire-resistant, but they are easier to break into than money safes. Therefore, valuables such as money and jewelry would be more easily stolen if they were stored in a record safe. On the other hand, a money safe would not protect company papers during a fire because the solid steel construction would heat the safe like a furnace.

Banks, factories, offices, and warehouses all need to be protected from theft. Many businesses have record safes for important papers or money. Banks have vaults for guarding cash, precious metals, and valuable possessions of their customers.

the lock is interfered with, the connection between the lock and bolt is easily broken. Once that happens, the safe door cannot be opened again.

Most record safes have key locks similar to those used to lock the doors of houses. Safes that are used to guard against theft usually have combination locks. A combination lock is a dial with letters or numbers on it, or both. A special combination of letters or numbers is needed to open the lock. It is almost impossible to open a combination lock by chance—a lock with four separate rings on the dial may have up to 100 million possible combinations.

Making safes burglarproof

Small safes, such as brick safes, can be set into a wall or a concrete floor to make them stronger. Large, free-standing safes are made of very strong steel alloys. Some are made from a single piece of metal, while others are made from several sheets of steel that are welded together.

The metal used to make safes is strengthened by adding hardened particles before the molten steel is cast into the shape of the safe. If a burglar tries to drill through the safe, the hard particles in the metal will chip and shatter most drill bits.

Some burglars use acetylene torches, fast drills, or explosives to penetrate a safe. However, all these methods of attack can be prevented by the design of the safe. A layer of copper in the safe wall spreads the heat away from the flame of an acetylene torch and makes it difficult to burn a hole through the wall of the safe. Copper can also resist some explosives. Most types of drills and explosives can be stopped by a layer of hard, fireproof material.

Many safes also have hidden hinges, so thieves cannot bypass the lock and take off the door by removing the hinges. Instead, the hinges, locks, and any other parts of the safe that could be easily attacked are enclosed in extra hard casings.

The one major drawback with safes is that they can be carried away to be opened elsewhere, or they can be opened by a really determined and well-equipped thief. This does not apply to vaults.

Vaults

Vaults hold large amounts of money and valuables, so they are at least the size of a small room. They are usually made of reinforced concrete and are strengthened with layers of copper and expanded steel mesh, which can stand up to drills. The doors on vaults can be up to 3 feet (1 meter) thick. The doors are usually tapered so that they fit perfectly into the wall and do not stick out at all. Some vault doors have as many as 16 bolts, each of which may be 3 inches (7.5 centimeters) thick or more.

Vaults are designed in a similar way to safes but on a much larger scale. Unlike safes, however, some vaults have controls to regulate the atmosphere inside. They adjust the humidity (the amount of moisture in the air) and the temperature inside the vault. As a result, items such as rare papers, paintings, and microfilm can be stored safely.

Because the vaults of banks need to be opened only during banking hours, most are equipped with time locks. Time locks can be opened only at set times. If the right combination is used when the bank is closed, the vault will still not open.

In one famous bank robbery in the south of France, burglars stole millions of dollars. They broke into the vault one weekend after digging a

▲ **Most doors are locked with one or two bolts. The doors on bank vaults have dozens of locks. The bolts are controlled by magnets and electric motors and cannot be opened by hand.**

tunnel from the building next door. Since then, most vaults are now built with detector strips in the concrete shell. These strips are connected to the bank's alarm system. Most successful robberies now involve bank officials being ordered to open the vault with threats of force to staff or family members rather than force to the vault itself.

See also: LOCK

Sailing

Wind power is one of the oldest ways of driving a boat. It is uncertain who first put sails on boats, but ancient pictures show wind power being used by sailors many thousands of years ago. Sailing boats move forward using the force of the wind in sails. Generally, the bigger the sails and the stronger the wind, the faster a sailing boat will move.

Before people discovered how to use sails, they had to rely on their own physical efforts to make boats move. Boats were rowed with wooden oars or, in the case of canoes, propelled using paddles. The invention of sailing removed the human effort from moving boats, allowing them to become much faster.

Early sailing boats

Old paintings show that the Egyptians were using large square sails to power boats as long ago as 3000 BCE. These sails were simply hung from a horizontal pole, or spar, fixed to a mast, and the boat would drift along with wind behind the sails blowing it forward. Large numbers of people and much cargo were carried in this way. The trouble with this drift sailing, however, was that boats could only travel in the desired direction when the wind blew from behind them. If the wind's direction changed, the boats could be blown off course.

It was not only the Egyptians who were learning to use the wind at this time. All around the world, sailors were experimenting with sails to power their boats. In South America, on Lake Titicaca, old pictures show boats made from reeds using sails of handwoven cloth. In China, sailors built sailing boats called junks. Junks have almost square sails that can be adjusted to suit wind direction, segmented wooden hulls for cargo, and large rudders for steering. Junks of virtually unchanged designs are still used by many Chinese sailors today.

Foreign trade

The early sailors traveled close to their own shores. Soon, however, sailors discovered that by traveling farther afield to countries overseas, they could buy unusual goods and earn money by bringing them home and selling them.

◄ *This sailing boat is being sailed by a Yemeni fisherman. The boat has a very simple design that has not changed for thousands of years. Simple, inexpensive sailing boats like this are still widely used in many developing countries.*

▶ *Most modern sailing ships, such as this yacht, are used for recreation. A crew of several people is usually required to sail a yacht, although some yachts are specially designed for single-handed sailing.*

Large trading companies wanted to take part in this sea trade. They immediately started to pay boatbuilders and sailmakers vast sums of money to make larger and faster boats. Cargo boats belonging to the different companies used to race across the oceans to be the first to bring home unusual and desirable goods, such as silks from India, and sell them for a large profit.

Bigger and better boats were designed with hulls that could slice smoothly through the water, and the number and size of sails on boats increased. Most important of all, boatbuilders and sailmakers began to design boats that could continue to sail in almost any conditions and could stick to their course, whatever the direction of the wind.

Until the turn of the twentieth century, great cargo sailing ships were seen all over the world. However, with the invention of the combustion engine, wind power gradually gave way to engine power. Today, people use sailing boats mainly for pleasure. Only in developing countries are sails still used to power boats for work and trade.

However, the desire to build ever-faster sailing boats still exists. Many millions of dollars are spent every year building racing yachts, similar to those that compete for the America's Cup. These boats now reach speeds that sailors in the past would never have dreamed possible.

Propulsion

A sailor uses the water, the shape of the boat's hull, and the sails to propel a boat forward. A sleek, smooth hull will cut through the water more easily and faster than a wide, box-shaped hull.

A boat in tidal water and traveling in the same direction as the tide will move faster than a boat doing the same speed but traveling against the tide. In fact, if a boat traveling in the opposite direction to the tide is going slower than the oncoming tide, it will end up going backward. The sailor calculates the speed, time, and direction of the tides and uses them to help move the boat along. The wind, though, is most important to the sailor. Sailors have more control over the wind than either the water they are sailing on or the shape of the boat. It is possible to control the wind through the sails. When the sails are set at the proper angle, the boat will move at the fastest speed possible.

A sail makes an airfoil shape, like an airplane wing, when the wind fills it. The side of the sail away from the wind is like the curved top of a wing.

Any object placed in a stream of air will disturb the normal air flow. When a sail enters an airstream, it forces the wind to curve around it. On the outside curve of the sail, the wind will have to move faster because it has farther to travel, so the wind pressure is reduced. On the inside curve of the sail, the pressure is increased because the air is covering a shorter distance. To make the boat move as fast as possible, the sailor aims to keep the most powerful wind pressure on the inside curve of the sail.

It is easy to understand how a boat can catch the wind in its sails when the wind is coming from behind the boat. The best sailors, however, manage to use the wind from almost any direction and still follow the direction they had planned.

Small boats and sailing dinghies nearly always have two sails. The sails have to be set so that they work together to help the boat along. No matter how many sails a boat carries, or how big or small the boat is, the same rules apply.

Features of a sailing boat

There are four main parts to a sailing boat. These are the hull, the sails, the centerboard (also called the keel), and the rudder.

The shape of the hull determines how well the boat cuts through the water. The sails catch the wind, which drives the boat along. The centerboard is the large fin that hangs from the bottom of the boat into the water. It holds the boat on course and helps prevent it from being blown sideways and toppled over. In dinghies and small sailing boats, the centerboard can often be raised and lowered. In larger sailing boats, this is not possible because the keel is too big and is weighted, usually with lead.

The final important part of the boat, the rudder, controls the course of the boat. The rudder looks rather like a fin and is positioned at the stern (back) of the boat. In smaller boats, a long pole, called a tiller, is used to control the rudder. In larger boats, it is controlled by a wheel. The sailor in charge of the boat, called the helmsman, normally controls the course of the boat and has charge of the rudder. The helmsman directs the course of the boat and tells the other people in the boat, called the crew, what they must do. A good helmsman should sail the boat at maximum efficiency but can be helped or hindered by the crew.

Points of sailing

The most important lesson any sailor ever learns is the points of sailing. This means knowing which course and which position the sails should be in at any given point.

If the boat is traveling with the wind behind it, for example, then the sails will be out at a right angle to the mast to catch as much wind as possible.

If the boat is sailing at an angle to the wind direction, but toward the wind, then the sails will be pulled in closely. The boat will probably be heeling

DID YOU KNOW?

Windsurfing, or boardsailing, combines aspects of sailing and surfing on a single-person craft called a windsurfer, or sailboard. Windsurfers were first developed in California in the late 1950s, notably by Jim Drake (a sailor) and Hoyle Schweitzer (a surfer). By the late 1970s, windsurfing had spread throughout North America and Europe. Windsurfers are popular because they are a comparatively inexpensive form of sailing and also because they are very fast and manuverable.

◀ *The smallest sailing craft are windsurfers. The surfer has to use his or her weight to counterbalance the sail against the wind. Horizontal ribs maintain the sail's shape to prevent it from collapsing.*

(leaning over), with the helmsman and crew leaning out on the opposite side from the sails to keep the boat as upright as possible.

When the boat is sailing toward the wind, it will have to adopt a zigzag course, called tacking, to make any headway (forward progress) into the wind. It is impossible to sail a boat with its bow (front) pointing directly in the direction the wind is blowing. If a sailor tries to do this, the sails flap, and the boat stops and becomes almost impossible to maneuver. This is called being "in irons."

Many sailing beginners find it difficult to master the points of sailing at first, but it soon becomes automatic, like riding a bike. After a while, most sailors can tell simply from the feel of the wind on their face or the ripples on the water exactly where the wind is coming from and how their boat should be adjusted.

Once the basic techniques of sailing have been mastered, there are all sorts of ways of increasing the speed of a sailing boat. Huge, usually brightly colored sails, called spinnakers, can be added in certain conditions to help the boat pick up more wind power. They take careful handling because they can collapse into the water and act like an anchor with the weight of the water they collect.

On some boats, the crew members hang by harnesses, called trapezes, over the edge of the boat with only their feet touching the sides. The suspended crew acts as a counterweight to help keep the boat upright when sailing into a strong wind.

Using these extra methods, boats can be forced to such a speed that only the very bottom of the hull is in contact with the water's surface. This is known as "planing." At this point, a sailing boat is on its way to becoming a racing yacht.

▼ *This illustration shows the three basic points of sailing. How a sailing boat adjusts its sails depends on the direction and strength of the prevailing wind. It is possible to sail against the wind by tacking.*

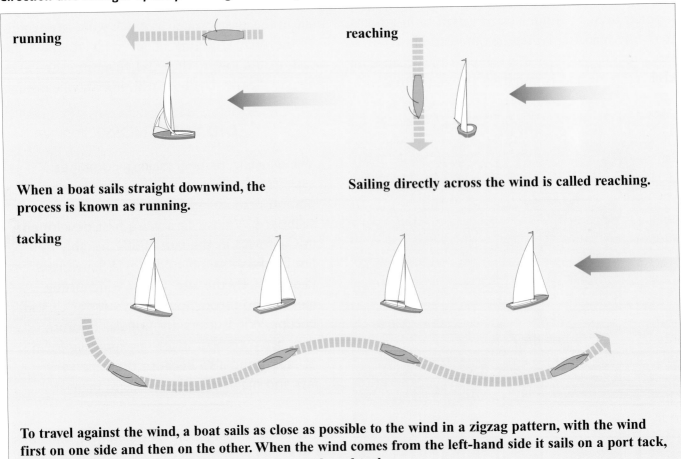

running

When a boat sails straight downwind, the process is known as running.

reaching

Sailing directly across the wind is called reaching.

tacking

To travel against the wind, a boat sails as close as possible to the wind in a zigzag pattern, with the wind first on one side and then on the other. When the wind comes from the left-hand side it sails on a port tack, and when it comes from the right it sails on a starboard tack.

Ocean-racing yachts cost many hundreds of thousands of dollars to build and are highly equipped racing machines. They are fitted with all kinds of extra equipment to ensure that the boat is being sailed efficiently. Computers provide information on the best set of the sails and the best course to be followed for maximum speed.

Racing yachts are built to be as light as possible so that they can plane easily through the water. Every ounce counts because top-level ocean races can be won or lost by a matter of seconds. Racing yachts are often made of artificial, composite materials, such as fiberglass or carbon fiber, that are very light and strong. They are also fitted with every possible device to increase their speed.

While no expense is spared on the boat, the crew has to endure uncomfortable conditions. No luxuries such as soft chairs or comfortable beds are allowed because they would increase the weight of the boat. The crew sleeps in bunks, and there are just enough so that the off-duty crew, called the off watch, can all sleep on the windward side of the boat (the side of the boat over which the wind is blowing). In this way, the off watch keep working while they sleep by helping to keep the boat balanced using the weight of their bodies.

The crew of ocean-racing yachts, particularly the most successful boats, works together like well-drilled soldiers, taking only seconds to change a set of sails or to adjust the sails for a new course.

The electronic equipment used on ocean racers, such as the computers, automatic helm controls, satellite navigators, and weather monitors are often as good as those found on modern cargo ships that travel around the world. Some cargo ships, however, are now using technology from sailing ships. Experiments are underway to develop cargo ships that can be used effectively with some form of sails once again.

The new era of sailing

In the 1970s, the Japanese led the way in developing new sail-bearing cargo ships and built the world's first sail-assisted tanker. Other countries are now experimenting with sail-bearing cargo ships.

▲ *The sailor in this picture is hanging over the edge of his sailing boat using a trapeze. By shifting his weight as far as possible in the opposite direction to the force of the wind, the boat remains as upright as possible.*

The reason for the interest in sail-bearing cargo ships is easy to understand. The fuel used to run the great engines that power modern cargo ships is becoming increasingly costly, while wind power is free. Operating cargo ships with sails can be much cheaper than using expensive fossil fuels.

In all cases, the new designs for sail-bearing cargo ships do not rely on wind power alone. The ships have both sails and engines, so they are known as sail-assisted ships.

In some cases, the sails are expected to be used only to add a little extra speed to a boat mostly under engine power. In other designs, the engines are used only for driving the boat in small and awkward spaces, such as harbors, or when there is no wind blowing, and the boat threatens to come to a stop in a flat calm. In these designs, the ship's engines can be greatly reduced in size.

In the past, one of the main drawbacks of sailing ships was that the sailors did not know what kind of weather to expect. The uncertainty made it impossible to know how long each voyage would take. Sailors today do not have these problems. Accurate weather forecasting and the use of

◄ This unusual looking boat is Planesail—the first wing-powered boat. Instead of fabric sails, the boat uses solid wings, similar to those of an aircraft.

Despite advances in sailing technology, wind still cannot be as reliable as an engine. Estimates for some sail-assisted ships claim that it would take around one hundred days for the round trip from England to Melbourne, Australia, and back again. This compares with 82 days taken by an engine-powered vessel, which can take a shortcut through the Suez Canal. A sailing ship would have to follow the prevailing winds right around Africa past the Cape of Good Hope. However, the savings in fuel costs can be considerable (well above 50 percent), so, from a commercial point of view, the extra journey time could be worthwhile.

Wingsails

As well as the recent mechanized modifications of conventional sails, other, more unusual types of sails have also been developed. These are called wingsails. A wingsail is more similar to the wing of an airplane than a sail. However, while an airplane wing is fixed horizontally, a wingsail is fixed vertically.

Unlike a sail, which constantly changes its shape, a wingsail maintains its airfoil shape. Therefore, it is better aerodynamically than a sail, and it can produce up to three times more drive than a sail for a given area. Another advantage of wingsails is that by using a second trailing element, like the tail of an aircraft, they automatically preserve the correct angle of attack to the wind at all times. This makes wingsails easier to handle than conventional sails.

However, there are also some problems with wingsails, which have limited suitability for many types of boats. The main problem is their weight. Although wingsails are made as light as possible, they are still much heavier than sails. Any weight carried up high makes a boat less stable. For this reason, most wingsail boats are wide, multihulled vessels, such as catamarans.

satellites means that ships are supplied with a minute-by-minute prediction of the conditions ahead. The captain of a sailing ship can take steps to avoid any unfavorable weather conditions and can adjust the ship's route as it goes along to take advantage of the wind that is available.

Another difficulty of sailing large ships in the past was that many sailors were required to climb up the masts to put up extra sails when the weather was good and take them down when it was bad. With modern sail-assisted ships, sails can be adjusted, furled, or unfurled on mechanized masts at the touch of a button. Computers keep a check on all the equipment, adjust it in the most effective way, and warn the captain of any sails that need repair or replacement.

The sails on sail-assisted ships are different from conventional sails. Although they are also usually made from canvas, they are large and rectangular and stretched taught by strong metal frames. There is often no rigging at all. Because the sails are intended to be used in conjunction with engines, the spread of sail is less than would be expected on a conventional sailing boat of the same size.

See also: MARINE PROPULSION • NAVIGATION • SHIP AND SHIPBUILDING • WIND

Salt, chemical

Most people use the word *salt* to describe common, or table, salt (sodium chloride), which is a seasoning agent and preservative added to food. In chemistry, however, *salt* refers to a large group of ionic compounds, of which common salt is just one example.

Many salts occur naturally on Earth. Common salt is often found near Earth's surface or buried in thick layers deep beneath the ground. Common salt also makes up a large proportion of the dissolved salts in seawater, along with bromides, chlorides, and the sulfates of magnesium and potassium. Many salts have been made by people. Examples include fertilizers, gunpowder, paint pigments, and washing soda.

Acids and alkalis

When some compounds are dissolved in water, they create a liquid called an acid. All acids contain hydrogen atoms. When acids dissolve in water, the hydrogen atoms lose electrons and turn into electrically charged particles called hydrogen ions (H^+). This process is called ionization. Examples of acids include hydrochloric acid (HCl) and nitric acid (HNO_3). When dissolved in water, HCl produces hydrogen ions (H^+) and chloride ions (Cl^-). Nitric acid produces hydrogen ions and nitrate ions (NO_3^-).

Alkalis are the opposite of acids. When alkalis dissolve in water, they often produce negative ions called hydroxide ions (OH^-). Examples of alkalis include sodium hydroxide (NaOH) and ammonia (NH_3). Sodium hydroxide produces OH^- ions and the positive sodium ion (Na^+) in water. Ammonia combines with hydrogen ions from the water to produce positive ammonium ions (NH_4^+) and hydroxide ions.

▼ *This photograph shows some of the salts formed when transition metals react with acids. Clockwise from upper left, they are: copper sulfate (blue), cobalt chloride (red), chromium chloride (dark green), iron chloride (brown), and nickel nitrate (green). One of the characteristics of the transition metals is that they form brightly colored salts.*

The metal zinc reacts with hydrochloric acid in a test tube. The reaction produces a salt called zinc chloride (ZnCl₂) and hydrogen gas (H₂), which can be seen bubbling through the solution.

Metals and acids

Some metals react with acids to produce hydrogen gas (H_2) and salt ions in a solution. For example, zinc dissolved in hydrochloric acid produces zinc chloride ($ZnCl_2$) and hydrogen gas. However, it is dangerous to add a reactive metal, such as sodium, to an acid. By contrast, some metals do not react with acids, especially if the acid is dilute (weak).

Naming salts

Most salts consist of metal ions and nonmetallic ions. The name of the salt is taken from the name of metal ion and the name of the acid before the reaction took place. Thus chloride salts come from hydrochloric acid, nitrates come from nitric acid, and sulfates come from sulfuric acid (H_2SO_4).

Reactions of acids and alkalis

When certain acids and alkalis mix in the correct proportion, they neutralize each other, producing a salt and water. During this so-called neutralization reaction, the hydrogen ions from the acid react with the hydroxide ions from the alkali to form water molecules. The positive ions of the alkali also react with the negative ions of the acid to form a compound called a salt. If the water is left to evaporate, the positive and negative ions bond to form crystals of the salt. When hydrochloric acid reacts with sodium hydroxide, a salt called sodium chloride forms, along with water. The reaction that takes place can be written like this:

$$NaOH + HCl \rightarrow NaCl + H_2O$$

The total number of positive and negative charges in a salt must add up to zero to keep the salt electrically neutral. However, some salts produce a slightly acidic or a slightly alkaline solution. For example, ammonium chloride (NH_4Cl) is slightly acidic when mixed with water, while sodium acetate (CH_3COONa) is slightly alkaline.

Different salts

There are roughly three kinds of salts: simple salts, double salts, and complex salts. Among the simple salts are common salt and sodium bicarbonate (bicarbonate of soda; $NaHCO_3$), which is used in baking powder and medicines. Sodium carbonate (Na_2CO_3), used in making ceramics, soaps, and other products, is another simple salt. So is potassium nitrate (KNO_3), which is used to make gunpowder. Simple salts contain a single metal ion.

Among the most important double salts are the alums. One of these, potassium aluminum sulfate (potash alum; $KAl(SO_4)_2$), is used in medicine, and it has also been used to fix dyes to fabrics. Roman scholar Pliny (23–79 CE) wrote that the Egyptians used potash alum to bind dyes to their cloth. Double salts contain at least two types of metal ions.

Complex salts such as potassium ferricyanide, which is used in dyeing and in fertilizers, have one metal ion bound to one or more chemical ions.

See also: ACID AND ALKALI • CRYSTAL • ION AND IONIZATION

Salt production

Common salt is found everywhere in the world. The oceans hold the greatest amount of common salt, but large salt layers are also found in Earth's crust, left when ancient seas dried up and were later covered with sand and soil. Large amounts of salt are mined from Earth and removed from seawater for use as a seasoning agent and preservative and as a raw material in the chemical industry.

Sodium chloride is the chemical name for common salt—so-called to distinguish it from other kinds of salts, such as acetates and sulfates. Common salt is a compound containing a shiny metal called sodium and a pale green gas called chlorine (NaCl). The familiar white crystals of common salt form when the two elements react.

Salt was once very valuable. It was used to preserve meat and fish before refrigerators were invented. Roman soldiers were given a regular allowance of salt, and the Latin word *salarium,* meaning "salt money," is where the English word *salary* comes from.

Besides its use in the home and in the food industry, common salt has many other uses. It is used to make chemicals such as chlorine gas (Cl_2) and hydrochloric acid (HCl), and it is also used in water softeners and as a deicer.

Salt in the earth

Common salt is found in thick layers under the ground. Some salt layers are very thick and cover a vast area. Underground salt, or rock salt, is mined like coal and other minerals by cutting the salt away in large, room-sized caverns. Thick salt pillars are left behind to hold up the roof of the cavern. The salt mine at Wieliczka, Poland, has been worked for seven hundred years. The salt from this mine is so pure that it needs no further purification.

Blasting and digging

In a typical salt mine, the salt rock face is cut at floor level by a heavy-duty rock-cutting machine to a depth of 12 feet (3.7 meters). Holes are then

◀ *A conveyor tips salt onto a huge pile at the Morton Salt Works at Inagua in the Bahamas.*

◄ *Workers collect salt from a salt pan in Hambantota, Sri Lanka. Salt is extracted from seawater in exactly the same way as Roman salt workers did more than two thousand years ago.*

drilled in the rock face, and these are filled with explosives. After the rock face is blasted, it shatters into about 1,000 tons (907 tonnes) of rock salt. The broken rock is taken to a conveyor belt that carries it through underground tunnels to a crushing machine. From there, the crushed rock salt is taken up to ground level.

Flooding and pumping

Another way to mine salt is to allow the salt pits to flood with water or to pump water into them. The salt then dissolves, and the resulting brine is pumped to the surface and allowed to dry. The problem with this method is that supporting pillars cannot be left behind, so there is the danger that the land covering the salt pit will collapse.

Drying salt in open pans

The oldest way of getting salt from brine is by the open-pan method. Early salt producers used pans made of pottery or lead. They were filled with brine and a fire was lit beneath them. The water turned to steam and disappeared, leaving behind the salt. Later, shallow steel pans were used, with brick ovens built underneath them. These were fired by coal. It was not a very efficient method, as it took about half a ton of coal to produce about one ton of salt.

By changing the temperature of the brine pans, different grades of salt can be made. The finest grade of salt is made by keeping the brine pan boiling and removing the salt as it forms. A thicker or coarser salt results from heating the brine at a lower temperature.

Sun-dried salt

In many countries, the Sun is used to evaporate seawater to form salt. Seawater is first channeled into large shallow ponds. There, clay and sand and other dissolved salts, such as calcium carbonate ($CaCO_3$), sink to the bottom. The brine is then channeled into smaller pans, called crystallizing pans. In these, salt of different grades is left behind—the finest grade in the first pan, coarser grades in the others.

Vacuum drying

Vacuum drying uses a series of closed tanks with a steam chamber, called a calandria, in them. Tubes through the chamber allow brine in the tanks to pass through the hot steam and circulate around the tank. When the brine in the first tank boils, the steam passes to the next tank. As the brine in the next tank boils, the steam passes to a third tank, and so on. The crystals are removed as they form in the bottom of the tanks. Further processing stages give rise to larger crystals of granular salt or spiky crystals of dendritic salt.

See also: MINING AND QUARRYING

Satellite

When the Soviet Union launched the world's first artificial satellite into orbit around Earth on October 4, 1957, the technology of sending it into space had been developed from the German rocket weapons of World War II (1939–1945). However, the complicated mathematics describing the motion of satellites around Earth had been determined more than three hundred years earlier.

In astronomy, a satellite is a small body that travels in orbit around a larger body. The Moon, for example, is a satellite of Earth. Most of the other planets have satellites, which are also called moons.

Saturn, for example, has no fewer than 22 moons. This article, however, concentrates not on these natural satellites, but on artificial satellites.

Understanding satellites and orbits

German astronomer Johannes Kepler (1571–1630) and English mathematician and physicist Isaac Newton (1642–1727) solved the problem of how the planets orbit the Sun. The same calculations show that an object can be made to stay in orbit around Earth if it is given just the right speed to balance Earth's gravity. The pull of Earth's gravity becomes less as an object moves farther away, so the speed it needs to stay in orbit becomes less, too.

▼ *This computer-generated image shows the satellite* Artemis *in orbit. Launched in 2001,* Artemis *has been designed to test new space technologies and promote new satellite services.*

▶ *This Delta rocket was launched in 1975 from Cape Canaveral, Florida. It carried Goddard's eighth Orbiting Solar Observatory. This satellite gathered data on energy transfer in the Sun's hot, gaseous atmosphere and investigated celestial sources of X-rays.*

Propelling a satellite through Earth's atmosphere and into orbit is complex. Too little speed, and the satellite will fall back to Earth. Too much speed, and it will escape altogether from Earth's gravity, moving off into space. The satellite must travel at exactly the right speed to enter Earth's orbit.

To stay in orbit at an altitude of about 150 miles (240 kilometers), a satellite must reach an orbital speed of 17,500 miles (28,000 kilometers) per hour. At this speed and altitude, a satellite would take about 90 minutes to orbit Earth. This time is called the orbital period. As the altitude of orbit increases, less orbital speed is necessary because gravity gets weaker farther away from Earth.

The orbital period increases with altitude. At an altitude of 1,000 miles (1,600 kilometers), the orbital period is two hours. At a height of 22,300 miles (35,900 kilometers), the orbital period is 24 hours. This fact is very useful for space scientists.

If a satellite is put into a 24-hour orbit directly over the equator (the imaginary line around Earth, midway between the North and South poles), and it is moving in the same direction that Earth is revolving, the satellite will move at the same speed as Earth underneath it. From the ground, the satellite will seem to hang at the same point overhead. This is called a geostationary or synchronous orbit. It is sometimes also called a Clarke orbit, after English science-fiction writer Arthur C. Clarke (1917–), who first suggested its usefulness for communications satellites. Communications satellites are placed in geostationary orbits so that they can maintain continuous contact with the same ground station.

Most satellites, however, are in low-Earth orbits (LEOs) between 200 and 500 miles (320 and 800 kilometers) high. Some are launched in polar orbits, in which they pass directly over the North and South poles. Many weather satellites are placed in polar orbits so that they can view the whole Earth spinning beneath them every 12 hours.

The first artificial satellites

The Soviet Union launched the first artificial Earth satellite into orbit on October 4, 1957. It was called *Sputnik 1*, and it was an aluminum sphere, about 2 feet (0.6 meter) in diameter, carrying a radio transmitter. It remained in orbit for 92 days, falling back to Earth on January 4, 1958.

On January 31, 1958, the United States launched its first satellite, called *Explorer 1*. Although it was much smaller than the early Soviet satellites, it made the first scientific discovery of the Space Age—it discovered that there are two intense "belts" of radiation around Earth. These radiation belts are now known as the Van Allen belts.

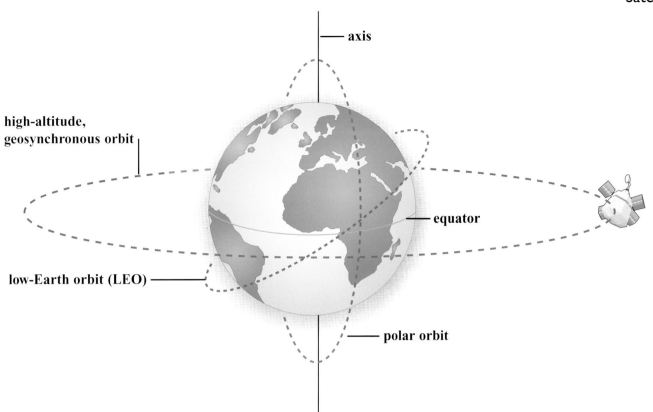

axis

high-altitude, geosynchronous orbit

equator

low-Earth orbit (LEO)

polar orbit

▲ *This illustration shows the three most common types of satellite orbits. A low-Earth orbit (LEO) is several hundred miles above Earth. A polar orbit is also an LEO, but it passes directly over the North and South poles. A high-altitude, geosynchronous orbit encircles Earth at an altitude of 22,300 miles (35,900 kilometers).*

Now, there are thousands of satellites from many nations orbiting Earth. Often, more than one hundred spacecraft are launched into Earth-orbit every year. These satellites do many useful things. They help improve communications between the continents, they provide information for meteorologists (weather forecasters), they help geologists search for minerals, and they allow astronomers to see into space more clearly.

Launching satellites

Until 1982, all satellites were launched by stage rockets—launch vehicles made up of a number of rockets joined end to end. However, in November 1982, two satellites were launched from the cargo bay of the Space Shuttle *Columbia*. Space shuttles are now a common means of launching U.S. satellites. Most satellites, however, are still launched using stage rockets. These are built in many different sizes to suit the various sizes of satellites. Other countries use stage rockets exclusively. For example, the European Space Agency (ESA) developed the successful three-stage Ariane series of rockets. Russia has developed a variety of stage-rocket launch vehicles, as have India and Japan.

Satellite lifetimes

In space, satellites may occupy a variety of orbits. The lowest orbit in which satellites fly is about 150 miles (240 kilometers) above Earth. At these low orbits, satellites have only a short lifetime because there is still enough air around a satellite to gradually slow it down. Once the satellite slows to below orbital speed, the pull of gravity makes it fall out of orbit. As the satellite reenters the thicker parts of Earth's atmosphere, it is heated by friction with the air. The satellite glows hotter and hotter and eventually burns up.

There is less air present at higher orbits, and a satellite has a longer life. In an orbit a few thousand miles high, a satellite could remain in space for several million years. However, a satellite usually has a useful working life of only a few years. Then it becomes a useless piece of "space junk."

At any one time, there are actually only a few hundred working satellites in orbit. Hundreds more are in orbit, but they are out of action for one reason or another. In addition, there are thousands of pieces of other space hardware floating around Earth, most of them parts of the launch vehicles that first put the satellites into orbit.

Satellite construction

Satellites differ widely in size and complexity. Some of the largest are communications satellites such as *Intelsat IX*, one of a series of satellites launched by the International Telecommunications Satellite Organization. *Intelsat IX* measures more than 20 feet (6 meters) across and had a launch weight of 5.2 tons (4.7 tonnes). Largest of all, however, are the piloted satellites, usually called orbiting space stations. These include the U.S. *Skylab*, Russian *Mir*, and the International Space Station.

Satellites also come in many different shapes and sizes. They often have instruments, cameras, and antennas protruding from them. They do not have to be streamlined as airplanes must be because they travel through space, where there is little or no air to cause resistance. The shape of satellites depends almost entirely upon their function.

However, satellites do share some of the same features. They are composed of certain subsystems. Each subsystem plays a vital role in making the entire satellite work. The basic structure is of aluminum or titanium, which carries the hardware of the other subsystems. These include communications equipment such as antennas, satellite dishes, radios, microwave transmitters, and recording equipment. This enables ground controllers or other ground systems to communicate with the spacecraft and allows the spacecraft to send information back to the ground. The transfer of information between a satellite and a ground station is often called telemetry.

▼ *A crew member from the Space Shuttle* **Endeavor** *attempts to capture the free-floating* **Intelsat VI** *communications satellite using the shuttle's satellite capture arm. Some large satellites are launched by space shuttles and may receive periodic repair and upgrading by astronauts.*

► *This picture shows* **Envisat,** *launched by the* **European Space Agency (ESA) in 2002. Envisat** *is an advanced polar-orbiting Earth observation satellite. It contains instruments for analyzing Earth's atmosphere, oceans, landmasses, and ice sheets.* **Envisat** *plays an important role in monitoring the evolution of environmental and climatic changes on Earth.*

The instruments form another major satellite system. They include all kinds of detectors to measure properties such as radiation and magnetism, as well as cameras and scanners of various kinds to take photographs and other recordings.

Another subsystem keeps the satellite in the correct attitude (position) using devices such as gyroscopes, Sun-and-star-tracking navigation equipment, and gas-reaction jets. Maintaining the correct attitude is vital for keeping the satellite's instruments pointing in the right direction.

The power to run the satellite's instruments, communications, and other electronic equipment comes from the electrical subsystem. Most satellites get their electricity from solar cells. These are semiconductor devices, mounted on large panels, which change the energy in sunlight directly into electricity. An array (set) of solar cells about the size of a tabletop would produce about a fourth of a kilowatt (250 watts) of power.

A few "spy satellites" are equipped with devices called radioisotope electric generators that produce nuclear power. These change the heat given out by radioactive materials, such as uranium or plutonium compounds, into electricity. They are a potential source of radiation pollution when they fall back to Earth. One Soviet nuclear-powered satellite, *Cosmos 1402,* caused alarm when it fell back to Earth early in 1983, but fortunately it fell into the sea.

Uses of satellites

The most useful of all satellites are those used to send radio, television, Telex, telephone, and other communications between continents. Many

▶ *This satellite image shows a view of California. Satellite images of Earth are enormously important to meteorologists and other Earth scientists. They provide a valuable perspective of Earth that has added greatly to the knowledge and understanding of our planet.*

countries have their own network of communications satellites, or comsats. Internationally, satellite communications are provided through the International Telecommunications Satellite Organization (Intelsat), established in 1964. Since 1982, a separate organization called the International Maritime Satellite Organization (Inmarsat) has set up a satellite network to provide communications for ships at sea. Many sailors, as well as other navigators, also now regularly use the international satellite-based Global Positioning System (GPS) to find their position.

Weather satellites are also of great benefit. From space, they get a much broader view of the weather systems on Earth, and they can relay weather data back continuously, day and night. Armed with such information, meteorologists use computers to predict how weather systems will develop. This helps them make more accurate forecasts.

A third kind of satellite is also making a valuable contribution to our knowledge of Earth. These are Earth-resources satellites, for example, the U.S. *Landsat*. These spacecraft have a system of electronic scanners that scan Earth's surface in light of different wavelengths. From these scans, images of the surface can be built up. These are combined

and printed in various colors to form what is called a false-color picture. The colors are selected so that certain surface features stand out.

In this way, it is possible to discover all kinds of things about Earth's surface that would otherwise go unnoticed. For example, areas of diseased crops can be pinpointed, new mineral deposits can be located, and sources of pollution can be identified.

Military spy satellites take even more detailed pictures of Earth. They use film or digital cameras with powerful telephoto lenses. Spy satellites using film cameras drop the fine-grain film to Earth in capsules after it has been used. The capsules are usually recovered by airplanes with grab nets.

Astronomical satellites are also very useful. They view space from high above Earth's atmosphere. From beneath the atmosphere, it is often difficult to see small astronomical details. These satellites can also view the heavens at wavelengths, such as X-ray and infrared, which Earth's atmosphere normally absorbs. Orbiting astronomical satellites have provided evidence of black holes and other planetary systems.

DID YOU KNOW?

The majority of satellites put into Earth-orbit every year are communications satellites. An increasing number of these satellites are for use by cellular phone networks. Cell phones work by transmitting call signals to a local ground station. These signals are then sent via satellites to the ground station in range of the person being called, and then to his or her phone.

See also: MOON • ORBIT • SPACE PROBE

Saturn

Saturn is the second largest planet in the solar system, after Jupiter. It is the easiest planet to recognize because of the wide rings that encircle it. These rings consist of ice-covered particles. Saturn is the sixth planet from the Sun and the farthest planet that can be seen from Earth without the help of a telescope.

Saturn was named for the Roman god of agriculture. It is the sixth planet from the Sun and one of the four gaseous outer planets called the Jovian, or Jupiter-like, planets. These giant gas planets do not have any solid surfaces and so are much less dense than the inner, rocky planets, such as Earth. In fact, if a large enough body of water could be found, Saturn would float on it.

Saturn is the second largest planet in the solar system, after its neighbor, Jupiter. In many ways Saturn is very similar to the giant planet Jupiter.

Both planets are large balls of mostly hydrogen (H_2) and helium (He) gas and are surrounded by clouds. Through a telescope, Saturn seems less colorful than Jupiter. It resembles a yellowish ball with some darker brown bands. Close-up images taken by space probes have shown that there are swirling cloud formations on Saturn, but they are usually hidden from view by high-altitude haze in the planet's atmosphere. Saturn has some of the fastest winds of any planet—they speed through the upper part of its atmosphere at 1,100 miles (1,800 kilometers) per hour.

Saturn is 75,000 miles (120,000 kilometers) in diameter across its equator, which is over nine times as wide as Earth's equator. However, Saturn's diameter from pole to pole is about 7,500 miles (12,000 kilometers) less than its equatorial diameter. This gives Saturn a somewhat squashed

▼ *This true-color image of Saturn taken from a Voyager space probe shows Saturn's major features. The planet's huge size, brightness, and wide system of rings make it the most recognizable and impressive planet in the solar system.*

shape. It is the least spherical of all the planets. At its equator, Saturn turns on its axis once every 10¼ hours. It actually spins more slowly closer to the poles because of its gaseous composition.

Saturn is, on average, 887 million miles (1,427 million kilometers) from the Sun, 9½ times as far away as Earth. Being so far away, it orbits very slowly, taking 29½ Earth-years to complete one trip around the Sun. Saturn is also very cold. The temperature at the top of its clouds is about –132°F (–180°C). Astronomers do not think that life of any kind could exist on Saturn.

Saturn's rings

The most spectacular feature of Saturn is its system of rings. Through a telescope on Earth, these rings appear as a thin, flat disk surrounding the planet's equator. There are actually three ring sections: the outer ring (A); the central ring (B), which is the widest and brightest; and the inner ring (C), which is also called the crepe ring because it is so

▲ *This artist's impression shows* **Voyager 1, which was the first of two space probes launched by NASA in 1977. Both Voyager probes passed Saturn, the first in 1980 and the second in 1981. They provided many of the first detailed images of the planet and its moons.**

DID YOU KNOW?

The first human-made object to encounter Saturn was the *Pioneer 11* spacecraft, launched by the National Aeronautics and Space Administration (NASA) in April 1973. *Pioneer 11* passed Saturn in September 1979. The *Voyager 1* and 2 spacecraft passed Saturn in 1980 and 1981 and carried equipment that provided closer examination and better images of the planet. *Cassini* was the most recent spacecraft sent to Saturn. It arrived in 2004 and carried a probe called *Huygens* sent to investigate Titan, one of Saturn's moons.

transparent that the globe of Saturn can be seen through it. The outer and middle rings are separated by a gap about 1,700 miles (2,700 kilometers) wide, known as the Cassini division.

After two Voyager space probes flew past Saturn in 1980 and 1981, astronomers discovered that Saturn's rings were even more complex in structure. In photographs taken by the Voyager cameras, Saturn's rings could be seen as 1,000 or more narrow ringlets and gaps that resembled the ridges and grooves of a phonograph record. Several threadlike ringlets were even found within the Cassini division. Astronomers still do not fully understand the appearance of Saturn's rings, but the gravitational pull of Saturn's moons is believed to be partly responsible for their existence.

The ring system is about 170,000 miles (270,000 kilometers) from side to side, but only about 300 feet (90 meters) thick. If the size of a CD were based on the same ratio of thickness to diameter as Saturn's rings, it would be about 2 miles (3 kilometers) in diameter.

Saturn's rings consist of countless rocky particles, ranging in size from pebbles to blocks the size of a house. They travel around the planet like tiny moons. The ring particles are thought to be coated with frozen gases, which makes them bright. The rings are either the remains of a former moon that

▼ *A computer-enhanced* **Voyager 2** *image shows the possible variations in chemical composition from part of Saturn's ring system. This image was assembled from clear, orange, and ultraviolet photographs.*

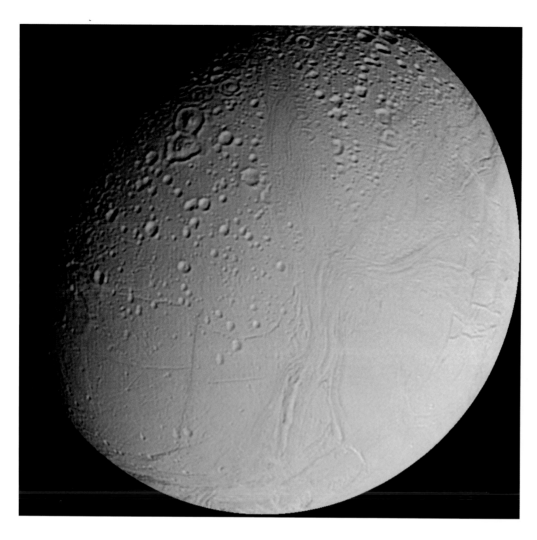

◀ *This Voyager 2 image shows Enceladus, which is one of the innermost of Saturn's moons. Enceladus displays varied types of terrain. Parts of the moon are cratered, while other areas show no signs of cratering. This suggests major geological activity in the recent past. There are also fissures (cracks), plains, corrugated (rippled) terrain, and other crustal deformations. This evidence suggests that the interior of Enceladus may still be liquid.*

broke up, shattered by the impacts of comets and meteoroids, or else they are part of a moon that never formed. Much of the elaborate structure of some of the rings is due to the gravitational effects of nearby satellites.

Saturn's moons

The Voyager probes discovered several previously unknown moons of Saturn, and several others have been discovered since. As of 2004, the total is 37. Most of these moons are small and insignificant, but the larger ones are of great interest. For instance, Mimas has a crater that is one-third of its 240-mile (390-kilometer) diameter. The impact that caused this crater must have come close to shattering Mimas to pieces. Another moon, called Iapetus, is half black and half white; one side is covered with dark dust from a nearby moon called Phoebe.

Titan is the largest of Saturn's moons, measuring 3,200 miles (5,120 kilometers) across, making it larger than the planet Mercury. Titan is half rock and ice and has a thick atmosphere made up mostly of nitrogen (N_2) and methane (CH_4), with orange-colored clouds on top. Beneath the clouds, a rain of liquid methane may fall onto a tarry surface. Titan is the only moon known to have a fully developed atmosphere and has often been described as a frozen version of Earth. The *Cassini* spacecraft, sent to Saturn in 1997, released a probe, called *Huygens*, in December 2004, which landed on Titan to examine this fascinating Moon in greater detail than ever before.

See also: ASTRONOMY • GRAVITY • JUPITER • MARS • MERCURY, PLANET • NEPTUNE • PLUTO • ROCKET • SOLAR SYSTEM • URANUS • VENUS

Scanner, image

> **Image scanners are devices that can analyze printed images or film transparencies and convert them into a digital format for manipulation and printing by computers.**

Image scanners have become important tools in many homes and offices. In the modern world of electronic media, images have to be in a digital format if they are to be viewed on screen, used by computers, or printed.

Some digital images are created inside computers using graphics software. Other images, such as photographs, may be imported by a computer already in a digital format, for example, images taken with digital cameras. Many types of images, however, need to be scanned to convert them into a digital format.

What scanners do

The basic principle of a scanner is to analyze an image and process it in some way to produce a digital representation of the image. The user can then save this digital image as a file on a computer. The image can then be manipulated using imaging software to produce the desired results. Imaging software may include photo-editing, desktop-publishing, or graphics packages.

Although many images are pictures, an image can also be text. Image scanners can be useful for scanning text. Optical-character-recognition (OCR) software recognizes any text in an image and creates an editable text file from it. OCR scanning saves having to retype paper-only text documents into a computer to use them on computer systems.

Types of image scanners

Image scanners come in many different shapes and sizes, but they fall into four main categories. Each type of scanner is designed for a particular use.

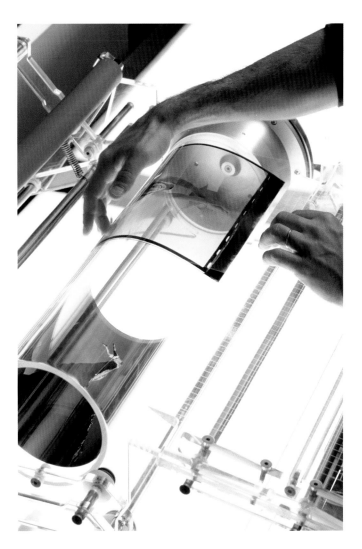

▲ *Drum scanners produce the very highest-quality scans, and are used for professional reproduction. The brightness and color of light reflected or transmitted by an image is analyzed by a photomultiplier tube to produce a digital copy of the image.*

Handheld scanners are the most basic type of scanner. As their name suggests, they are small devices operated by hand. The image to be scanned is held still while the scanner is moved slowly over the surface. Handheld scanners are simple reflective scanners. They can only scan images that reflect light, such as photographs or other printed images. The benefits of handheld scanners are their low price and portability, but they cannot produce the same quality results as the other types of scanners.

Sheet-feed scanners resemble desktop printers. Images are fed mechanically through the scanner past a fixed scan head. Sheet-feed scanners are also just reflective scanners and can only scan printed images. They can produce reasonable quality scans, but quality is often limited by scan speed. Sheet-feed scanners have the advantage that they can automatically scan batches of images and, therefore, are often set up for fast, multiple scanning, particularly of text images.

Flatbed scanners (also called desktop scanners), are the most common type of image scanner. They are widely used both in homes and offices. Flatbed scanners consist of a horizontal scanning "bed" with a clamshell lid that closes over the top of the image.

The simplest flatbed scanners are reflective only. However, more advanced scanners are both reflective and transmissive. Transmissive scanners have the ability to scan images that allow light through, for example, film transparencies. The ability to scan transparencies, as well as versatility and high scan quality, have made flatbed scanners the poplar choice. Basic flatbed scanners are also reasonably inexpensive, although price can vary considerably as size and performance increase.

Drum scanners, as the name suggests, use a cylinder, or "drum," onto which images are mounted for scanning. Drum scanners work in a completely different way from other types of scanners. They can produce incredibly detailed scans from both reflective and transmissive images. Drum scanners are professional devices used largely by the publishing industry. The large size and high cost of drum scanners make them unsuitable for most users.

How an image scanner works

Aside from specialized drum scanners, most other scanners analyze images in the same basic way. They do this using charge-coupled devices (CCDs). The main differences between the various types of scanners is in the way images are held and moved past their scan heads.

CCDs comprise thousands of tiny, light-sensitive diodes, which convert photons (light particles) into electrons (electrical charge). These diodes are called photosites. The brighter the light that hits a photosite, the greater the electrical charge that it produces. The pattern of electrical charge across the CCD represents the pattern of brightness of the image.

The CCDs in scanners are arranged into a long strip called an array. As the CCD array moves across an image, it detects light reflected from, or shone through, the image.

> ## DID YOU KNOW?
>
> To communicate with computers, image scanners need to be connected using an interface. Three main interface standards exist. TWAIN is generally the most widely used, although the newer Scanner Access Now Easy (SANE) interface is becoming more popular because of its greater flexibility. Image and Scanner Interface Specification (ISIS) is used by most professional image scanners.

▶ *Handheld scanners have the benefit of being very portable. They are often used in conjunction with laptop computers. Scans from handheld scanners are of low quality, however, and it is difficult to avoid unwanted hand shake as they are used.*

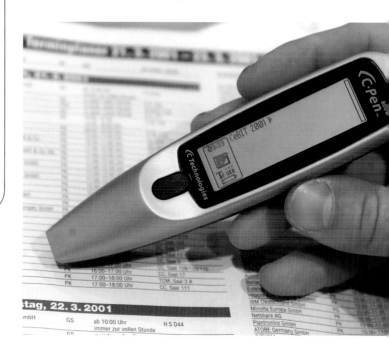

◄ *Flatbed scanners are the most common type of image scanner. They can be used to scan documents as well as transparencies. Flatbed scanners are available in different sizes and specifications. Many are relatively inexpensive and are popular with home users. Other flatbed scanners cost many thousands of dollars and rival the quality of drum scanners.*

In a flatbed scanner, a lamp is used to illuminate the image. The light from the image reaches the CCD array through a series of mirrors, filters, and lenses. The entire mechanism (lamp, mirrors, filters, lenses, and CCD array) make up the scan head. The scan head moves slowly across the image by a belt that is attached to a stepper motor. This moves the scan head past the image in fixed "steps." A scan is made of the image at each step until the whole document has been covered. The scanner's software then combines the step scans to produce the complete image.

Light from the image is reflected by angled mirrors. Each mirror is slightly curved. By curving the mirrors, the images they reflect are focused onto a smaller surface. The final mirror reflects the image onto a lens. The lens focuses the image through a color filter onto the CCD array.

The arrangement of mirrors, filters, and lenses varies between scanners, as does the method of their operation. Most scanners now use a single-pass scanning method. In this method, lenses split the reflected image into three smaller versions. Each smaller version passes through a color filter (either red, green, or blue) onto a specific section of the CCD array. The scanner's software then combines the data from the three parts of the CCD array and produces a single, full-color image.

Photomultiplier tubes

Drum scanners work in a different way from the other types of scanners. Instead of using a CCD sensor, they use a photomultiplier tube (PMT). The document to be scanned is mounted on a glass cylinder. At the center of the cylinder is a sensor that splits light reflected from, or transmitted by, the document into three beams. Each beam passes through a color filter (red, green, or blue) and then into a photomultiplier tube, where the light is changed into electrical signals. PMTs have a broader dynamic range than CCDs, meaning they can detect differences in brightness across a wider range. This broader dynamic range enables PMT scanners to capture a greater amount of detail.

See also: OPTICS • PHOTOCOPIER • PHOTOGRAPHY, DIGITAL

Seismology

Seismology is the study of earthquakes and the waves they create in the ground. Scientists use instruments called seismographs to detect and record these waves and to help them tell when and where large earthquakes will occur. Geologists also purposely create small earthquakes to study the structure of Earth's crust.

Earthquakes are among the most destructive events in the natural world. They can occur in many parts of the world, seemingly without warning. Earthquakes have caused widespread destruction in civilizations throughout history. In North America, two massive earthquakes have occurred within the last century. One earthquake destroyed most of San Francisco in 1906, killing more than 3,000 people, and the other earthquake devastated Anchorage and Valdez in Alaska in 1964, claiming 125 lives.

Central America also experiences serious earthquakes. One that shook Guatemala in 1976 decimated villages and towns and left nearly 25,000 people dead. A few months later, over half a million people were killed by an earthquake in and around the cities of Beijing, Tangshan, and Tianjin in China. Italy, Iceland, Turkey, Japan, the Philippines, and Indonesia also experience devastating earthquakes.

Quaking earth

Several hundred thousand earthquakes occur every year. Most are so mild they are undetectable, except by using instruments called seismometers. Many are felt but cause little damage. A few, however, have frightening power, equal to that of several hundred atomic bombs exploding simultaneously.

The energy of earthquakes is often measured on the Richter scale. Earthquakes above 3 on the scale can be felt by human beings. Above 5 on the scale, serious damage occurs. At 8 or above, destruction in the area closest to the earthquake is total. The Alaska earthquake of 1964 measured 8.6 on the scale and was one of the largest ever recorded. The scale most widely used to measure the surface intensity of earthquakes is the Mercalli scale, which ranges from 1 to 12.

◀ *The San Andreas Fault extends along the coast of northern California. The difference in terrain on either side of the fault line is a result of the fault's lateral movement over the centuries.*

◄ *This "real time" earthquake monitoring station is at the Museum of Natural History, New York. Using live seismic data from around the world, the station allows visitors to see for themselves the active nature of Earth's surface.*

Seismic waves

Most earthquakes take place at a depth of less than 25 miles (40 kilometers) below the surface. The actual site of the earthquake is called the focus. The point on the ground immediately above the focus is called the epicenter. In regions close to the epicenter, the ground may actually crack and open up, and it is there that the ground vibrates the strongest. Vibrations also travel through the rocks in Earth's crust and shake the ground violently many miles around the epicenter.

These vibrations are known as seismic waves. Scientists think there are several types of seismic waves. The one that travels fastest is the P-wave, the primary (pressure) wave. The P-wave travels in the same way as a sound wave—it vibrates in the same direction as it is traveling.

The other main type of wave is the slower S-wave, the secondary wave. It is also called the shear wave because it vibrates from side to side and causes rocks to shake and shear (slide past each other). L-waves, or long waves, are the third type of seismic wave. Divided into L (I) and L (II) waves, these are also called surface waves, because they travel slowly in the upper surface layers. Due to their large amplitudes (wave sizes), L-waves are the most powerful and destructive shock waves.

There are several hundred seismic stations throughout the world. When an earthquake occurs, these stations record the waves reaching them at different times. By sharing their results, they can pinpoint exactly where the earthquake occurred. Worldwide, seismic data are gathered and processed by the International Seismological Centre in England. There, a large computer calculates exactly where and how the earthquake occurred.

DID YOU KNOW?

Worldwide, there are up to one thousand earthquakes every month. Most are too small to be felt, and only a few each year are big enough to cause serious damage.

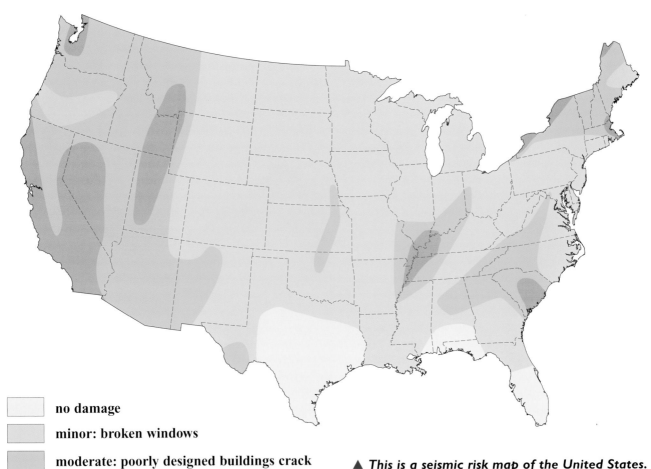

no damage

minor: broken windows

moderate: poorly designed buildings crack

major: buildings collapse, roads destroyed, landslides

▲ *This is a seismic risk map of the United States. Each zone refers to the maximum earthquake intensity recorded and, therefore, to the maximum destruction that could occur.*

Geologists themselves may also create small earthquakes to set up seismic waves in the ground. They drill holes to various depths in the ground and set off explosions within them. They record the ground waves from these explosions using seismometers, and from the results they can determine the structure of the underlying rock layers. This process is called seismic surveying and is often used when searching for oil and mineral deposits.

Scientists have studied the structure not only of Earth but also of other bodies in the solar system. The Apollo astronauts took seismic equipment to the Moon in the late 1960s and early 1970s. The Viking probes that landed on Mars in 1976 also carried seismometers on board. These instruments reported that there is very little seismic or volcanic activity on either the Moon or Mars. They also revealed that the structures of these two bodies are different from Earth's structure.

Seismographs

Most seismometers measure seismic activity using a pen recorder, which makes a permanent record of the measurements. These seismometers are called seismographs. The record (tracing) made is called a seismogram. To properly record movements of Earth's crust, seismic observatories must use a seismograph that measures horizontal movement and another that measures vertical movement.

The horizontal seismograph uses a heavy weight (up to 1 ton or 0.9 tonnes) on a pendulum and is based on the principle of inertia. The pendulum is actually a weighted horizontal beam. It is pivoted to a fixed frame and suspended from it by wire. When the ground shakes, the frame shakes, too, but the heavy weight tends to remain where it is. This causes movement between the weight and the frame, which makes the recording pen record a trace on a moving roll of paper.

The vertical seismograph also has a weight on a pivoted horizontal beam, but it is suspended from its frame by a spring. Stretching of the spring measures vibrations in the ground.

Ground tremors (vibrations) are usually very small, so the relative movement of the weighted pendulum must be amplified. Earlier seismographs used a system of levers or mirrors ("optical" levers). Today, electromagnetic seismographs are widely used. Coils surround the weighted pendulum, which is located within a magnetic field. When the weight moves, a minute current is set up in the coils by electromagnetic effect. This type of device also records seismic movements on a tape for analysis by a computer.

Modern seismology

In the future, seismologists may be able to reduce the loss of life from earthquakes. Damage is usually the result of poor construction or building on soft

seismogram

> **DID YOU KNOW?**
>
> The earliest known device used for detecting earthquakes was made in China in 132 CE. It was an urn with metal balls balanced around its rim. When there was a tremor, one of the balls would fall into a holder, making a loud noise.

ground, which can increase shaking many times. This factor caused buildings to collapse in the bayside Marina district of San Francisco during an earthquake in 1989, even though it was 50 miles (80 kilometers) from the center of the earthquake.

Predicting earthquakes precisely is very difficult. Experts had been expecting the 1989 San Francisco earthquake for some years but could not say exactly when it would happen. Many people feel that there would be more danger in issuing frequent false alarms. Instead, seismologists are concentrating on helping engineers and planners to avoid dangerous ground and to use construction methods that will withstand earthquakes.

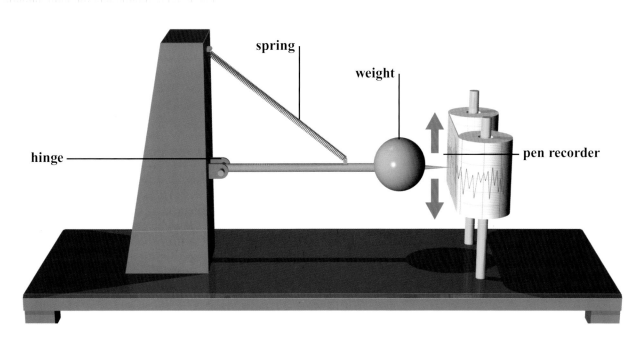

▲ *This inertial seismograph uses the displacement of a weight connected to a pen recorder to draw a seismogram of vertical ground motion. The seismogram shows seismic waves associated with the earthquake.*

See also: EARTHQUAKE • GEOLOGY • PENDULUM • VOLCANO

Glossary

Aerodynamic Referring to the shape of an object that allows for a minimal disturbance of air flow around it.

Alpha rays High-speed alpha particles emitted during the energetic radioactive decay of certain atoms. Alpha particles consist of two protons and two neutrons, forming a helium nucleus.

Ammeter An instrument for measuring either direct (DC) or alternating (AC) electrical current, in amperes.

Centrifuge An apparatus that spins liquids or solids at high speeds, forcing the heavier parts out to the edge and keeping the lighter parts nearer the center, thus separating them.

Ceramics Certain types of hard, nonmetallic, crystalline solids. China and silicon are ceramics.

Composite A material that is strengthened by the addition of other materials.

Current In a wire, a measure of the quantity of electrons passing any point of the wire per unit of time. Current is usually measured in amperes.

Diffuse For particles in liquids and gases to move from areas of high concentration to areas of lower concentration so that the particles become more evenly distributed.

Electrons Subatomic particles (particles smaller than atoms) that have a negative electrical charge.

Frequency The rate at which something occurs or is repeated, as in the number of pulses in radio waves or the number of times an alternating current flows back and forth in an electric circuit.

Gravity The natural force of attraction exerted by a massive body, such as Earth, upon objects at or near its surface, tending to draw the objects toward the center of the body.

Hormones Chemicals secreted into the blood by ductless glands and carried to specific cells, organs, or tissues to stimulate chemical activity.

Inertia The state of matter that prevents it from moving when it is at rest or from stopping or changing course when it is moving in a straight line unless an outside force is applied.

Liquid One of the four states of matter (the others are solid, gas, and plasma). Liquids have no fixed shape but take the shape of their containers; however, liquids do have a fixed volume.

Magnetism An invisible force that draws together some metals, such as iron, or pushes them apart. Magnetism is one of the basic forces of nature, and it is closely related to electricity.

Nanotechnology The manipulation of matter, such as individual molecules, on the nanometer scale. One nanometer is one-billionth of one meter, or 10^{-9} meters.

Nutrients Substances that are beneficial to the existence and development of living organisms.

Organic Containing carbon and hydrogen, often in conjunction with other elements, such as nitrogen and sulfur.

Proteins Large organic molecules containing nitrogen. Proteins are formed from combinations of amino acids.

Radioactivity The spontaneous disintegration of unstable nuclei, which is accompanied by the emission of particles or rays.

Ratio The relationship between two amounts involving the number of times one amount contains the other. In a ratio of 2:1, for example, there is twice one amount than the other.

Rheostat An adjustable resistor used to adjust current or vary the resistance in electric circuits.

Semiconductor Any class of crystalline solids intermediate in electrical conductivity between a conductor and an insulator. Semiconductors are used to control an electrical current.

Synthetic Of or related to materials manufactured to imitate natural products.

Vacuum A space entirely devoid of matter, or more generally, a space that has been exhausted to a high degree by an air pump or other artificial means.

Voltmeter A device for measuring volts. Volts are units of measurement of electrical force.

X-ray Short-wave electromagnetic radiation produced when speeding electrons hit a solid target.

Index

Page numbers in **bold** refer to main articles; those in *italics* refer to illustrations.